# Writing & Grammar

## Grade 8

### CARNEGIE LEARNING

PITTSBURGH, PA

*Writing & Grammar*

Care has been taken to verify the accuracy of information presented in this book. However, the authors, editors, and publisher cannot accept responsibility for Web, e-mail, or newsgroup subject matter or content, or for consequences from application of the information in this book, and make no warranty, expressed or implied, with respect to its content.

**Trademarks:** Some of the product names and company names included in this book have been used for identification purposes only and may be trademarks or registered trade names of their respective manufacturers and sellers. The authors, editors, and publisher disclaim any affiliation, association, or connection with, or sponsorship or endorsement by, such owners.

**Literary Credits:**
*Writing*
"Working on the Moon" from *First on the Moon: A Voyage with Neil Armstrong, Michael Collins, and Edwin E. Aldrin Jr.* Written with Gene Farvmer and Dora Jane Hamblin. Copyright © 1970 by Little, Brown and Company Inc. By permission of Little, Brown and Company.

"Indian Castle" from IIndians of the PlainsI by Eugene Rachlis. Copyright © 1960 by American Heritage Publishing Company, Inc. Reprinted by permission of American Heritage Publishing.

From *Immigrant Kids* by Russell Freedman, copyright © 1980 by Russell Freedman. Used by permission of Dutton Children's Books, a division of Penguin Young Readers Group, a member of Penguin Group (USA) Inc. 345 Hudson Street, New York, NY 10014. All rights reserved.

ISBN 978-1-53384-177-3

© by Carnegie Learning, Inc.
501 Grant St., Suite 1075
Pittsburgh, PA 15219
E-mail: info@carnegielearning.com
Web site: www.emcschool.com

Printed in the United States of America

27 26 25 24 23 22 21 20     3 4 5 6 7 8 9 10

# CONTENTS

# Unit 7

# Unit 8

## Common Usage Problems

## Writer's Workshop: Building Effective Sentences

# PART I

# **WRITING**

Name: _____  Date: _____

# Tell About a Conflict

**Narrative writing** tells a story or describes events. Examples of narratives include both works of fiction, such as short stories and novels, and works of nonfiction, such as historical accounts and personal letters and journals. In most narratives, the events are presented in the order in which they happened, or **chronological order.**

What makes a narrative interesting is the **conflict,** or struggle, between two forces. There are two types of conflict: external and internal. In an **external conflict,** the main character struggles against another character, against the forces of nature, against society, or against fate. In an **internal conflict,** the main character struggles against some element within himself or herself.

## Learn from a Literary Model

Read the following passage from "The Treasure of Lemon Brown," a short story by Walter Dean Myers, on pages 16–26 of your textbook. Note the forces struggling with each other and how they react as the conflict develops. To this point in the story, a boy, Greg, takes a walk and enters an abandoned building. There he meets an old man, Lemon Brown, who often speaks of having a "treasure." Two would-be robbers enter the building, prepared to take away the man's treasure.

### from The Treasure of Lemon Brown, by Walter Dean Myers

"Hey! Ragman!" a voice called. "We know you in here. What you got up under them rags? You got any money?"

Silence.

"We don't want to have to come in and hurt you, old man, but we don't mind if we have to."

Lemon Brown squeezed Greg's hand in his own hard, gnarled fist.

There was a banging downstairs and a light as the men entered. They banged around noisily, calling for the ragman.

"We heard you talking about your treasure." The voice was slurred. "We just want to see it, that's all."

… "There's another room over there; I'm going to take a look. You got that flashlight?"

"Yeah, here, take the pipe too."

Greg opened his mouth to quiet the sound of his breath as he sucked it in uneasily. A beam of light hit the wall a few feet opposite him, then went out.

"Ain't nobody in that room," a voice said. "You think he gone or something?"

*States source of conflict and identifies two opposing forces*

*Includes several lines of dialogue to reveal more of conflict*

*Action and detail help build suspense*

*Details intensify sense of danger*

*Adds to building tension*

*Dialogue brings scene to life*

"I don't know," came the answer. "All I know is that I heard him talking about some kind of treasure. You know they found that shopping-bag lady with that money in her bags."

…There was a footstep on the stairs, and the beam from the flashlight danced crazily along the peeling wallpaper. Greg held his breath. There was another step and a loud crashing noise as the man banged the pipe against the wooden banister. Greg could feel his temples throb as the man slowly neared them. Greg thought about the pipe, wondering what he would do when the man reached them—what he *could* do.

*Series of actions moves conflict forward*

… "There he is!" a voice cried from below.

"Throw down your money, old man, so I won't have to bash your head in!"

Lemon Brown didn't move. Greg felt himself near panic. The steps came closer, and still Lemon Brown didn't move.

*Revealing character's emotional state adds to increasing tension*

…Greg wet his lips, put his hands to his mouth, and tried to make a sound. Nothing came out. He swallowed hard, wet his lips once more, and howled as evenly as he could.

*"What's that?"*

As Greg howled, the light moved away from Lemon Brown, but not before Greg saw him hurl his body down the stairs at the men who had come to take his treasure. There was a crashing noise, and then footsteps. A rush of warm air came in as the downstairs door opened; then there was only an ominous silence.

*Conflict is resolved with daring action*

… "Mr. Brown?" he called.

"Yeah, it's me," came the answer. "I got their flashlight."

## Questions on Conflict

1. Who are the opposing forces?

   _____

2. What is the source of the conflict?

   _____

3. How does the reader know what the conflict is about?

   _____

4. Copy a sentence from the passage that reveals an emotional reaction from a character, and explain how the reaction reinforces the conflict.

   _____

5. The last long paragraph includes a number of actions to bring the conflict to a climax. List a few of them.

   _____

*Writing & Grammar*

## On Your Own

Read the following passage from "Flowers for Algernon," a short story by Daniel Keyes, on pages E30–E54 of your eBook. To this point in the story, Charlie has undergone an experimental operation that increases his level of intelligence. However, his factory coworkers are unaware of the type of operation that was performed.

### *from* Flowers for Algernon
### by Daniel Keyes

**PROGRESS REPORT 11**

**April 30** I've quit my job with Donnegan's Plastic Box Company. Mr. Donnegan insisted that it would be better for all concerned if I left. What did I do to make them hate me so?

The first I knew of it was when Mr. Donnegan showed me the petition. Eight hundred and forty names, everyone connected with the factory, except Fanny Girden. …

"Which don't mean to say," she remarked, "that I don't think there's something mighty strange about you, Charlie. Them changes, I don't know. You used to be a good, dependable, ordinary man—not too bright maybe, but honest. Who knows what you done to yourself to get so smart all of a sudden. Like everybody around here's been saying, Charlie, it's not right."

"But how can you say that, Fanny? What's wrong with a man becoming intelligent and wanting to acquire knowledge and understanding of the world around him?"

She stared down at her work and I turned to leave. Without looking at me, she said: "It was evil when Eve listened to the snake and ate from the tree of knowledge. It was evil when she saw that she was naked. If not for that none of us would ever have to grow old and sick, and die."

1. What is the source of the conflict?

   _____

2. What types of conflict are evident in this passage?

   _____

3. How do you know that Charlie is questioning the decision that he made to undergo the operation?

   _____

4. What emotional reaction does Fanny have to Charlie's changed behavior? How does her behavior indicate how she is feeling?

   _____

# Your Assignment
## Narrate a Conflict

To complete this assignment, follow the five stages of the writing process:

# ① Prewrite

Before you write, gather your thoughts and plan your narrative.

## Select a Subject to Write About

In choosing a conflict to narrate, think in terms of the two types of conflicts:

### External
- *person against person*, such as one player against another in a game. The conflict need not be physical. That is, the conflict may be a battle of wills, such as a parent and child in strong disagreement.
- *person against nature*, such as someone caught in a storm or a strong tide
- *person against society*, such as an outsider trying to fit into a different culture

### Internal
- *person against herself or himself*, such as an individual who is struggling to decide on the best course of action

On the lines below, list four conflicts you might narrate.

_____   _____

_____   _____

Think about each of these conflicts. Consider the character(s), the source of the conflict, and the actions, details, and dialogue you can use to reveal the conflict and move it forward. Consider, too, the type of narrator you will use to tell the story. Remember that a **first-person narrator** is one of the characters in the story; he or she participates in the action of the narrative. A **third-person narrator** is outside the story; he or she observes the action of the narrative.

Choose one conflict from the four you listed and write it below. Also jot down who will narrate the story.

_____

## State Your Purpose and Identify Your Audience

For everything you write, you should consider why you are writing it and who will be reading it. Your purpose and audience will determine what you write and how you write it.

For example, if you are narrating a conflict as part of a story, your purpose is to entertain and keep the reader interested. If you are narrating a conflict as a means of making a point to someone, your purpose is to persuade.

The student writing about the car accident during the snowstorm wanted to tell an exciting story that will hold readers' attention and thus entertain them. She wrote this statement of purpose and audience:

> My purpose is to narrate a tension-filled story that will make readers anxious but that they will enjoy reading.

Write a sentence stating your purpose and audience on the lines below.

_____

_____


## Gather Your Information

Before you write, gather information about your conflict. Use the following categories to help you take notes:

Setting                    Forces
Narrator                   Sources of conflict
Characters' emotions       Actions

The student narrating the story about the car accident made these notes:

| | |
|---|---|
| Setting: | In a van driving on a winding country road; a nighttime snowstorm |
| Narrator: | Teenager in the story |
| Characters' emotions: | Mom—tense |
| | Teenager—playful, tense, relaxed |
| Forces: | Mother and teenager driving in a van through a snowstorm |
| Source of conflict: | Snowstorm, car accident |
| Actions: | Snow falling heavily |
| | Phone call to Dad |
| | Peering through partially covered windshield |
| | Car coming head-on |
| | Van goes off the road |
| | Teenager takes the wheel and drives to hospital |
| | Mom's head is bleeding |
| | Teenager wraps Mom's head |


## Organize Your Information

Now that you have gathered your information, consider how best to organize it for your narrative. In most cases, the events or actions in a narrative are organized in **chronological order,** or the order in which they happened. It usually makes sense to tell a story from beginning to end.

Determine the order of occurrence of the "Actions" you wrote down, and number them accordingly. The student writing about the car accident reviewed her list of "Actions" and numbered them as shown here:

Actions:   Snow falling heavily ①

Phone call to Dad ③

Peering through partially covered windshield ②

Car coming head-on ④

Van goes off the road ⑤

Teenager takes the wheel and drives to hospital ⑧

Mom's head is bleeding ⑥

Teenager wraps Mom's head ⑦

## ② Draft

In drafting your narrative, put your information into sentence and paragraph form. Begin your narrative with an introduction that will capture your reader's interest and set the stage for the action. As you develop the body of the narrative, focus on the action of the conflict, supplementing it with details of setting, dialogue, and characters' emotions as needed. End with a conclusion, showing how the conflict is resolved.

## ③ Revise

Be sure to allow yourself time after drafting to revise. During the Revise stage, evaluate the information you provided and the organization you followed. Have you told a good story? Will your audience be interested in how the conflict is developed and resolved?

Use the questions in column 1 of the Revision Checklist to identify areas that need improvement. Then, based on the evaluation, revise your draft. Use the suggestions in column 2 to fix the problems you have identified.

In revising your draft, you may decide to add, delete, or rearrange information to strengthen the story you are telling. Remember that your goal is to narrate a conflict, describing the actions or events and the emotions of the characters participating in them. Following chronological order, or the order in which events occurred, usually makes sense in a narrative.

Read a printout of your draft, and mark your changes on the paper as you go. Think about whether your narrative identifies, develops, and resolves the conflict in a way that readers will understand and enjoy.

 **REVISION CHECKLIST**

| Evaluate | Strengthen |
|---|---|
| ☐ Does your introduction engage the reader and set up the conflict? | Write an introduction that hooks the reader and focuses attention on the conflict. |
| ☐ Does your narrative describe a conflict? | Write a narrative that clearly describes a conflict, or struggle between two opposing forces. |
| ☐ Does your narrative have a consistent narrator? | Maintain a consistent narrator, or point of view, throughout the story. |
| ☐ Does your narrative use actions to develop the conflict and move the story along? | Provide a series of actions that are easy to follow and that move the conflict forward. |
| ☐ Does your narrative use dialogue and descriptive details to supplement the actions? | Use dialogue and descriptive details to give necessary background information and clarity to the actions. |
| ☐ Does your narrative reveal the emotions of the characters? | Describe the emotions of the characters to intensify the conflict for the reader. |
| ☐ Does your narrative end with a strong conclusion? | Wrap up the conflict with a powerful resolution. |

# Grammar & Style: Commas

Using commas correctly and consistently is difficult for many writers. Knowing when to add a comma after a word or clause at the beginning of a sentence can be especially confusing. (Remember that a **clause** is a group of words with a subject and a verb that functions as one part of speech.)

As a general rule, commas are used to separate words and thoughts for the purpose of clarifying meaning. Include a comma after an introductory word or clause to help ensure readers will comprehend that beginning part of the sentence before reading the rest of it. Review these examples, in which not having a comma after the bold word or clause confuses the meaning of the sentence:

**However** I was able to help with the project.

**Since the deadline had passed in May** we didn't expect to hear any news.

**Even so** it would have been thoughtful to let us know.

In each case, adding a comma after the introductory word or phrase will make readers pause and absorb its meaning before reading on.

You may have noticed in reading different kinds of materials, both in school and out, that some authors use a lot of commas and some use only a few. Many modern writers, in particular, leave out commas after introductory words and phrases, taking a "less is more" approach. Doing so is fine, as long as the meaning is clear and there is some consistency in comma use.

**Exercise:** Insert the comma where necessary in each of the following sentences.

1. Because the show ran late we got home after midnight.

2. Whenever I think too much my head hurts.

3. However we should make plans soon.

4. When spring arrives people seem to be reborn.

5. Since you left I have been so bored at home.

Now review your narrative to see if you used commas properly following introductory words and clauses.

# ④ Edit and Proofread

After you have revised your draft, edit it to check your spelling, punctuation, and grammar for errors. You may have found some of these kinds of errors already in the Revise stage, but read through your narrative again to look for errors more carefully.

Also review your draft to look for ways to improve the narrative power of your writing. Think of how you can help readers follow the story and feel the emotions of the characters involved in the conflict. Also check your use of commas with introductory words and clauses. Review the Grammar & Style lesson for guidelines about using commas correctly.

Retype or rewrite your narrative, making all of the changes you marked in editing. Then check the accuracy of this edited draft by doing a final proofread. Having a classmate read your work is a good way to find any remaining errors.

Also reread your draft to make sure it meets the requirements of a narrative about a conflict, as listed in the Writing Rubric below. Check off each item that applies to your story.

Review the Original Student Draft and the Revised/Edited Student Draft to see the process one student followed in drafting and then revising and editing/proofreading her narrative.

 **WRITING RUBRIC**

A successful narrative of a conflict has these qualities:
- ❏ Starts with a compelling introduction
- ❏ Tells of two opposing forces struggling against one another
- ❏ Reveals the source of the conflict
- ❏ Ends with a strong conclusion
- ❏ Uses a consistent point of view, or narrator
- ❏ Incorporates actions, dialogue, descriptive details, and setting
- ❏ Reveals the emotions of the characters
- ❏ Uses commas properly following introductory words and clauses
- ❏ Uses correct spelling, grammar, punctuation, and vocabulary

Did you check off each item? If not, consider making additional changes to your narrative.

## Original Student Draft

Mom and I thought we could make it out to the farm and back before the snowstorm hit. But it took a while for her to decide on the antique table she wanted and to get it loaded into our van. By the time we got back on the road, the snow had already covered the road.

By then the sun was completely gone and the snow was falling in big, wet flakes. It was falling so fast the windshield wipers could not keep up with it. Mom had to lean forward to peer through the snow-covered glass. She drove the van slowly around one curve after another.

"Get on your cell phone," she said, without moving her eyes from the road, "and call Dad. Tell him where we are."

I made the call. Before I had a chance to say anything, Dad yelled, "Where are you?"

"We're on the way home from Jensen's farm."

"Why'd you go out there on a day like today?" he asked. "Let me talk to your mother."

She could hear Dad's loud, excited voice, and said, "I can't talk now."

"She has to pay attention to the road," I said. "We'll be home soon." Then I added, more for my sake than his, "Don't worry." I hung up.

"Good," Mom said.

But just then as we were going into a sharp curve a car coming in the other direction came around the curve on the wrong side of the road. Mom swerved to avoid the car and did, but we wound up off the road and up a small embankment.

"Mom, are you okay?" I asked.

She was slumped over the wheel. "Mom!" Blood flowed freely from her forehead. I took her scarf and wrapped it tightly around her forehead to slow the bleeding. I managed to slide her over from the driver's seat to the passenger seat. She tried to stop me, saying, "I'm okay. I'm okay." But I could see she wasn't.

I buckled her into her seat belt and lowered the seat back, thinking the blood would not flow so fast. I got out of the van and looked over the situation.

I sat myself in the driver's seat and slipped the van into reverse. Slowly, slipping a little, the big van got us back on the road. "Now all I have to do is drive us to the hospital," I thought.

## Revised/Edited Student Draft

Mom and I thought we could make it out to the farm and back before the snowstorm hit. But it took a while for her to decide on the antique table she wanted and to get it loaded into our van. By the time we got back on the **main** road, the snow had already covered the **white line on the curving country** road.

By then the sun was completely gone and the snow was falling in big, wet flakes. It was falling so fast the windshield wipers could not keep up with it. Mom had to lean forward to peer through the snow-covered glass. **With her hands locked on the steering wheel, sS**he drove the van slowly around one curve after another.

"Get on your cell phone," she said, without moving her eyes from the road, "and call Dad. Tell him where we are."

**"Where are we?" I asked, trying to lighten things up.**

**"Don't try to be funny," she said. I was beginning to feel nervous.**

Uses first-person point of view throughout

Adds descriptive details

Inserts dialogue to reveal tense emotional state of character

I made the call. Before I had a chance to say anything, Dad yelled, "Where are you?"

"We're on the way home from Jensen's farm."

"Why'd you go out there on a day like today?" he asked. "Let me talk to your mother."

She could hear Dad's loud, excited voice, and said, "I can't talk now."

"She has to pay attention to the road," I said. "We'll be home soon." Then I added, more for my sake than his, "Don't worry." I hung up.

"Good," Mom said.

But just then, as we were going into a sharp curve, a car coming in the other direction came around the curve on the wrong side of the road. **It headed straight at us.** Mom swerved to avoid the car and did, but we wound up off the road and up a small embankment.

*Adds comma*

*Adds action to build suspense*

"Mom, are you okay?" I asked.

She was slumped over the wheel. "Mom!" **I reached over and lifted her head from the steering wheel.** Blood flowed freely from her forehead. I took her scarf and wrapped it tightly around her forehead to slow the bleeding. I managed to slide her over from the driver's seat to the passenger seat. She tried to stop me, saying, "I'm okay. I'm okay." But I could see she wasn't.

*Adds action to show logical sequence of events*

I buckled her into her seat belt and lowered the seat back, thinking the blood would not flow so fast. I got out of the van and looked over the situation. **"If we can back down from this hill," I thought, "and back onto the road, we might have a chance."**

*Adds internal dialogue to reveal emotional state and thinking of character*

I sat myself in the driver's seat and slipped the van into reverse. Slowly, slipping a little, the big van got us back on the road. "Now all I have to do is drive us to the hospital," I thought. **"No problem," I said to myself.**

## ⑤ Publish and Present

- Draw a sketch that captures the conflict in your narrative.
- Stage a skit of your narrative, involving several classmates and simple props.

## INFORMATIVE WRITING
# Write a Coherent Informative Essay

An **informative essay** is a written work of multiple paragraphs that explores a topic with the goal of informing or enlightening the reader. In a well-written informative essay, the writer makes clear how sentences and paragraphs are connected, leading the reader from one idea to the next.

    **Coherence** is the word used to describe this quality of connectedness or unity in writing. In a coherent piece of writing, the ideas flow naturally and logically from one another, just as the pieces in a puzzle connect to create a picture.

## Learn from a Literary Model

Read the passage below, which is an excerpt from the informative essay "Working on the Moon," on pages 131–132 of your textbook. This essay was written by American astronaut Edwin Aldrin Jr., who gives a firsthand account of exploring the moon during the 1969 *Apollo 11* mission. Notice how the organization of Aldrin's essay makes it easy for readers to follow his ideas and therefore understand his explanation of what it was like to work on the moon

### from **Working on the Moon, by Edwin Aldrin Jr.**

The moon was a very natural and very pleasant environment in which to work. It had many of the advantages of zero-gravity [weightlessness], but it was in a sense less *lonesome* than zero G, where you always have to pay attention to securing attachment points to give you some means of leverage. In one-sixth gravity, on the moon, you had a distinct feeling of being *somewhere*, and you had a constant, though at many times ill defined, sense of direction and force.

*States main idea in opening sentence*

*Second sentence states main idea of paragraph*

One interesting thing was that the horizontal reference on the moon is not at all well defined. That is, it's difficult to know when you are leaning forward or backward and to what degree. This fact, coupled with the rather limited field of vision from our helmets, made local features of the moon appear to change slope, depending on which way you were looking and how you were standing. The weight of the backpack tends to pull you backward, and you must consciously lean forward just a little to compensate. I believe someone has described the posture as "tired ape"—almost erect but slumped forward a little. It was difficult sometimes to know when you were standing erect. It felt as if you could lean farther in any direction, without losing your balance, than on earth. By far the easiest and most natural way to move on the surface of the moon is to put one foot in front of the other. The kangaroo hop did work, but it led to some instability; there was not so much control when you were moving around.

*Provides strong topic sentence to indicate main idea of paragraph*

*Uses transitions (That is, This fact) to link sentences*

*Repeats word erect to reinforce topic for readers*

As we deployed our experiments on the surface we had to jettison things like lanyards [short cords], retaining fasteners, etc., and some of these we tossed away. The objects would go away with a slow, lazy motion. If anyone tried to throw a baseball back and forth in that atmosphere he would have difficulty, at first, acclimatizing himself to that slow, lazy trajectory [path]; but I believe he could adapt to it quite readily.

*Provides strong topic sentence to indicate main idea of paragraph*

*Gives example from common experience (baseball) to help readers understand*

Technically the most difficult task I performed on the surface was driving those core samplers into the ground to get little tubes of lunar material for study. There was a significant and surprising resistance just a few inches down. But this resistance was not accompanied by a strong supporting force on the sides. What this meant, quite simply, was that I had to hold on to the top of the core tube extension while I was hitting it with the hammer to drive it down into the ground. I actually missed once or twice. It wasn't a question of visibility. In bringing the hammer down, I tended to disturb my own body position and my balance. One explanation for the strange degree of resistance may be that, having already been compressed by the lack of atmosphere, it has been continually pounded by meteorites. This pounding probably has compacted that lower material much further, to a point where additional compacting—like that of forcing a cutting tool and tube through it—requires significant applications of force….

*Provides another strong topic sentence*

*Repeats word resistance several times to help readers follow discussion*

*Repeats words hammer, pounded/pounding, compacted/compacting, and forcing/force to guide readers*

Odor is very subjective [personal], but to me there was a distinct smell to the lunar material—pungent, like gunpowder or spent cap-pistol caps. We carted a fair amount of lunar dust back inside the vehicle with us, either on our suits and boots or on the conveyor system we used to get boxes and equipment back inside. We did notice the odor right away.

*Provides strong topic sentence for new paragraph*

*Uses common examples of smells to help readers relate*

It was a unique, almost mystical environment up there.

*Restates main idea*

1. What is the main idea of Aldrin's essay, as stated in the first paragraph?

   _____

   _____

2. In each of paragraphs 2, 3, 4, and 5, Aldrin states the main idea of the paragraph in its topic sentence. In your own words, state the main idea of each paragraph.

   Paragraph 2: _____

   Paragraph 3: _____

   Paragraph 4: _____

   Paragraph 5: _____

3. **Transitions** are words and phrases that show readers the link between what has been said and what will follow. In paragraph 2, how does the transitional phrase *That is* link the first and second sentences?

_____

_____

4. In paragraph 4, Aldrin repeats the word *resistance*, helping readers stay focused on this topic through a series of sentences. What other words does he repeat in this paragraph, and how does repeating them help readers follow the explanation?

_____

_____

5. In paragraph 2, Aldrin helps readers understand what it's like to throw something on the moon by using the example of throwing a baseball—something most people have done. In paragraph 5, how does he help readers understand what lunar material smells like?

_____

_____

6. How does the last paragraph relate to the ideas Aldrin discusses previously in the essay?

_____

_____

## Your Assignment
### Write a Coherent Informative Essay

To complete this assignment, follow the five stages of the writing process: Prewrite, Draft, Revise, Edit and Proofread, and Publish and Present.

## ① Prewrite

Before you write, gather your thoughts and plan your essay.

### Select a Subject

In choosing a subject to write about, consider people, places, things, and ideas that you know well enough to explain in five or so paragraphs. For example, consider these subjects: being a teenager, my favorite activity, relatives of mine, and my neighborhood. Be sure your subject is one that you can *explain*, because you are writing an informative essay.

List four subjects you might write about.

_____

_____

_____

_____

Think about the various qualities or parts of each of these subjects. What would you need to explain about each subject to help readers understand it? For example, for the subject *being a teenager*, you might explain the privileges that come with being a teen and also the responsibilities. For the subject *my neighborhood*, you might write about the types of homes, schools, and businesses in the area and the people who live and work there.

Consider each subject and what you would need to explain about it. Choose one subject and write it down here.

_____

## State Your Purpose and Identify Your Audience

For everything you write, you should consider why you are writing it and who will be reading it. Your purpose and audience will determine what you write and how you write it.

For example, if you are writing about being a teenager to show your parents that you understand the responsibilities and privileges you have, then you will have to provide information to which your parents can relate and to explain it in a serious, straightforward way. If, however, you are writing about being a responsible or privileged teenager to give your friends a laugh, you will probably use different information and present it in a silly or humorous way. In both cases, however, you will be explaining your subject.

One student decided to write an informative essay about her neighborhood. She wrote this statement of purpose and audience:

> I will explain what my neighborhood is like to someone who has never been there.

Write a sentence stating your purpose and audience.

_____

## Gather Your Information

Before you write, gather information about your subject. To do so, brainstorm a list of the information you will need to provide to explain your subject. Begin with general qualities or ideas, and then get more and more specific. To organize your ideas, use a chart like the one below.

The student writing about her neighborhood started by thinking of the general qualities of the area, such as the homes, the people, the businesses, and the schools.

She wrote these qualities across the page, using them as column headings. Then she listed specific details under each heading, creating a chart.

## Essay Planning Chart

| Homes ① | People ④ | Businesses ② | Schools ③ |
|---|---|---|---|
| Some new homes—big Ⓒ | Some young families—mostly in new homes Ⓓ | Gas station has been there a long time Ⓐ | Old elementary school closed—now community center Ⓐ |
| Some old homes—small Ⓐ | Many older people—mostly in older houses Ⓐ | KwikMarket added to gas station Ⓑ | New school built on edge of town Ⓑ |
| Some people have added on to old homes Ⓑ | Have known older people a long time—don't see them much Ⓒ | Used to be small grocery store and shops—torn down, new houses built Ⓒ | Kids used to walk to school—now take bus Ⓒ |
| | Older people's families have grown up—moved away Ⓑ | | |

## Organize Your Information

Now that you have gathered your information, consider how best to organize it into an essay. Think about what order will be most effective in explaining your subject to your audience.

One common plan for organizing an informative essay is to end with the best or strongest point. Look at your Essay Planning Chart. Do you have more information or better information in any of the columns? Would it make sense to give any of this information before or after other information?

The student writing about her neighborhood noticed that she had the most details listed in the "People" column of her chart. She also noticed that some of the things she planned to say about the people were tied to information in the "Homes," "Schools," and "Businesses" columns. Based on these observations, the student decided to write about the people in her neighborhood last. She numbered the columns of her chart 1, 2, 3, and 4, as shown in the sample.

Looking at the details listed under each column heading made the student realize that she had a lot of information about how her neighborhood had changed during the time she had lived there. She decided to organize these details using a "then versus now" pattern, first discussing how things used to be and then discussing how things are today. She labeled the details under each column heading A, B, C, and so on.

Use a similar system of numbers and letters to organize the information in your Essay Planning Chart. Keep in mind that your purpose is to explain your subject to your readers.

## Write Your Thesis Statement

Review your statement of purpose/audience against the information you have gathered and the plan you have created for organizing it. Like the student writing about her neighborhood, you probably have a more specific purpose in mind, now that you have done more thinking about and planning for your subject.

Try rewriting your original purpose/audience statement so that it provides a specific statement of your main idea. For example, the student who decided to write about how her neighborhood had changed rewrote her purpose/audience statement as follows:

> Many things have changed in my neighborhood while I've lived there, including the homes, the businesses, the schools, and the people.

In an essay, the main idea is called the **thesis statement.** It is usually stated at the beginning of the essay and then supported or proven by the information given in the rest of the essay.

Write your thesis statement here.

_____

_____

## ② Draft

In drafting an essay, follow this three-part format: introduction, body, and conclusion.

### Introduction

Your first paragraph, which is the **introduction,** should identify your subject and capture your readers' attention. Consider what will get readers interested and make them want to read more. Possible attention-getters include the following:
- an interesting fact or statistic about the subject
- a short story about a personal experience with the subject (whether your or someone else's experience)
- a quotation or statement from someone who knows about the subject
- a description or definition of the subject

After getting readers' attention, tell them what your essay will be about by giving them your thesis statement.

### Body

In the **body** of your essay, present the information you gathered and organized in the Prewrite stage. Use this information to support or prove the thesis you stated in your introduction.

For each column head in your Essay Planning Chart, write a sentence that states the point you want to make about this topic. For instance, for the essay about her changing neighborhood, the student wrote this sentence about the "Schools" topic:

> My neighborhood doesn't have its own elementary school anymore.

Use this sentence as the **topic sentence** for a paragraph about this idea. Write additional sentences for the paragraph using the details you listed under the column head. Each additional sentence should somehow prove or support the idea stated in the topic sentence.

*Writing & Grammar*

The body of your essay should have three or four paragraphs like this, in which you state and then prove or support an idea. And each body paragraph you write should prove or support the thesis you stated in your introduction. Making these connections among all the elements of your essay will help ensure that it is coherent.

## Conclusion

The **conclusion** of your essay should be a short paragraph that restates the main idea of the essay, which is your thesis statement, and provides a sense of finality or closure. Consider what final thought or idea you want your readers to have.

## ③ Revise

Be sure to allow yourself time after drafting to revise. During the Revise stage, evaluate the information you provided and the organization you followed. Have you clearly explained your topic? Will your readers be able to follow your explanation?

Use the questions in column 1 of the Revision Checklist to identify areas that need improvement. Then, based on the evaluation, revise your draft. Use the suggestions in column 2 to fix the problems you have identified.

In revising your draft, you may decide to add, delete, or rearrange information to strengthen your explanation. Remember that your goal is to connect the information in a way that will make sense to readers.

Read a printout of your draft, and mark your changes on the paper as you go. Think about whether your essay presents a coherent explanation that readers will understand.

 REVISION CHECKLIST

| Evaluate | Strengthen |
|---|---|
| ☐ Does your introduction begin with an attention-getter? | Create interest by beginning with an interesting fact, story, quotation, or description. |
| ☐ Does your introduction present a clear thesis statement? | Add or revise your thesis to provide a clear statement of your main idea. |
| ☐ Does each paragraph in the body treat a different part or quality of the topic? | Review your planning chart and follow the organization you developed there. |
| ☐ Does each paragraph in the body begin with a topic sentence and then provide supporting details about it? | Begin each paragraph with a topic sentence that states a main idea, and add or revise other sentences to prove or support it. |
| ☐ Does the conclusion restate the thesis and provide some sense of closure or finality? | Restate your thesis in different words, and provide readers with some final thought about your subject. |

# Grammar & Style: Clear Use of *This*

The word *this* is a **pronoun,** which means it takes the place of a **noun.** To use *this* or any pronoun correctly, however, the noun it replaces must be clearly identified in advance (usually, in the previous sentence or earlier in the same sentence). That noun is called the **referent.**

Not having a clear referent makes it difficult for readers to follow the ideas presented. Here are some examples of vague pronoun use:

The surface had been compressed by the lack of atmosphere and pounded by one meteorite after another. *This* has probably compacted the lower material.

Astronauts must study and train to work on the moon. *This* is something I'd like to know more about.

To what does *This* refer in each example? Several nouns are mentioned in each first sentence, so the referent is unclear. Adding a noun after *This* helps make the meaning clear, as shown in these examples:

The surface had been compressed by the lack of atmosphere and pounded by one meteorite after another. *This pounding* has probably compacted the lower material.

Astronauts must study and train to work on the moon. *This preparation* is something I'd like to know more about.

Clarifying pronoun references is an effective way of making your writing more coherent.

**Exercise:** Rewrite each of the following sentences so it's clear to what the pronoun *this* refers. In reading each sentence, ask "This *what?*" If the answer is not obvious, insert the word or words needed to make the thought clear.

1. The acrobats performed their routine with grace and strength. This won over the audience.

2. In 1940, the entire town was destroyed by a huge fire. This would not happen today.

3. Some people rush in making decisions, but this does not have to be disastrous.

4. The doctor had studied at several hospitals and universities and done research around the world. This helped her get a position with the state health department.

Now go back to your draft and look at each sentence. See if you need to correct any vague uses of *this* or other pronouns.

## ④ Edit and Proofread

After you have revised your draft, edit it to check your spelling, punctuation, and grammar for errors. You may have found some of these kinds of errors already in revising your draft, but read through it again to look for them more carefully.

Also review your draft to look for ways to improve the coherence of your writing. Think of how you can link the ideas in your essay, leading readers from one point to the next. In particular, use transitions and repeat key words to make important connections. Also look at your use of *this* and other pronouns to make sure they have clear referents. Review the Grammar & Style lesson for guidelines about using *this* clearly.

Retype or rewrite your informative essay, making all of the changes you marked in editing. Then check the accuracy of this edited draft by doing a final proofread. Reading your essay out loud is a good way to find any remaining errors.

Also reread your draft to make sure it meets the requirements of an informative essay, as listed in the Writing Rubric below. Check off each item that applies to your essay.

Review the Original Student Draft and the Revised/Edited Student Draft to see the process one student followed in drafting and then revising and editing/proofreading her informative essay.

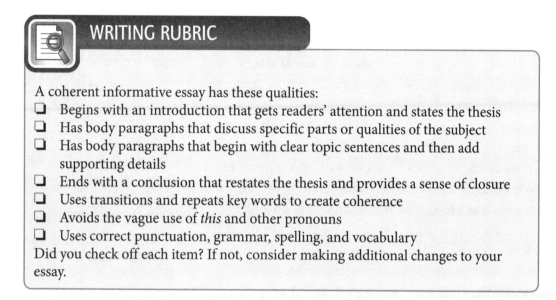

## WRITING RUBRIC

A coherent informative essay has these qualities:
- ❑ Begins with an introduction that gets readers' attention and states the thesis
- ❑ Has body paragraphs that discuss specific parts or qualities of the subject
- ❑ Has body paragraphs that begin with clear topic sentences and then add supporting details
- ❑ Ends with a conclusion that restates the thesis and provides a sense of closure
- ❑ Uses transitions and repeats key words to create coherence
- ❑ Avoids the vague use of *this* and other pronouns
- ❑ Uses correct punctuation, grammar, spelling, and vocabulary

Did you check off each item? If not, consider making additional changes to your essay.

## Original Student Draft

Many things have changed in my neighborhood while I've lived there, including the homes, the businesses, the schools, and the people.

My neighborhood today has a mixture of old and new homes. The older homes like mine are very small. Because of this, some people have added on to them. The new houses that have been built are twice as big as the old houses.

The gas station on the corner of Webster and Lake has been there a long time. A KwikMarket was added to it a few years ago. There used to be a grocery store and some other shops in the neighborhood. They have been torn down. New houses have been built in their place. Everyone goes to the SuperMart and the mall now.

My neighborhood doesn't have its own elementary school anymore. The old Westwood School closed three years ago. It became a community center last year. A new elementary was built on the edge of town, so it's not in a neighborhood. No kids walk to school anymore. They all take the bus.

The people in my neighborhood have changed, too. Most of the older people who are still there live in the small, older houses. Their families have grown up and moved away. I have known these people my whole life. I don't see many of them very often. Some younger people have moved into the neighborhood. Most of them live in the newer, bigger homes. A lot of them have children that go to the new elementary school.

Many things have changed in my neighborhood while I've lived there.

### Revised/Edited Student Draft

**My parents bought our house on Webster Avenue just before I was born. They thought this neighborhood had all the things that would make it a good place to raise a family.** Many things have changed in my neighborhood while I've lived there, including the homes, the businesses, the schools, and the people.

My neighborhood today has a mixture of old and new homes. The older homes like mine are very small. Because of ~~this~~ **their small size,** some people have added on to them. The new houses that have been built are twice as big as the old houses.

**There are fewer businesses in my neighborhood than there used to be.** The gas station on the corner of Webster and Lake has been there a long time. A KwikMarket was added to it a few years ago. There used to be a grocery store and some other shops in the neighborhood~~.~~**, but T**~~t~~hey have been torn down~~.~~ **and N**~~n~~ew houses have been built in their place. Everyone ~~goes to shops~~ **shops at** the SuperMart and the mall now.

My neighborhood doesn't have its own elementary school anymore. The old Westwood School closed three years ago~~. It~~ **and then** became a community center last year. A new elementary **school** was built on the edge of town, so it's not in a neighborhood. No kids walk to school anymore. They all take the bus.

The people in my neighborhood have changed, too. Most of the older people who are still there live in the small, older houses. Their families have grown up and moved away. **Even though** I have known these people my whole life~~.~~, I don't see many of them very often. Some younger people have moved into the neighborhood~~.~~**, and M**~~m~~ost of them live in the newer, bigger homes. A lot of them have children that go to the new elementary school.

Many things have changed in my neighborhood while I've lived there. **I still like living there, though, and hope my family never moves.**

*Adds personal story to introduction for attention-getter*
*States thesis*

*First body paragraph has clear topic sentence*

*Clarifies use of this*

*Adds topic sentence to second body paragraph*
*Uses transitions but and and to connect sentences*

*Repeats word shops*

*Third body paragraph begins with topic sentence*
*Adds transition words to link sentences*
*Repeats word school*
*Fourth body paragraph begins with topic sentence*
*Adds transition words and phrases to link ideas and combine sentences*

*Adds sentence to provide closure or final thought*

## ⑤ Publish and Present

- Exchange essays with a classmate. As you read one another's work, write down questions about things that seem unclear. Then discuss how to fix these problems. Does more information need to be added, or does the writing need to be made more coherent?
- Find another informative essay in your textbook or another source. Read through it, and then review it against the Writing Rubric in this lesson. Does the essay have all the qualities of a coherent informative essay? Present your evaluation to a small group of classmates.

## DESCRIPTIVE WRITING
# Describe a Character

Creating memorable characters in writing depends on the author's ability to describe someone so well that readers can visualize his or her appearance, mannerisms, and actions. The act of creating or describing a character is called **characterization.**

Authors use three main techniques to form a character:
- describes the physical features, dress, and personality of the character
- shows what the character says, does, and thinks
- shows what other characters say or think about him or her

Combining these techniques creates a profile of a character that enables readers to feel as though they know the person being described.

## Learn from a Literary Model

The following excerpt is from Maya Angelou's autobiography *I Know Why the Caged Bird Sings*, on pages 177–184 of your textbook. The excerpt is about a woman named Mrs. Flowers, who lived in Stamps, Arkansas, in the 1930s and was a mentor for Angelou. As you read, note how Angelou uses details about Mrs. Flowers's appearance and actions to help convey her personality.

### from **Mrs. Flowers,** *in* **I Know Why the Caged Bird Sings, by Maya Angelou**

Mrs. Bertha Flowers was the aristocrat of Black Stamps. She had the grace of control to appear warm in the coolest weather, and on the Arkansas summer days it seemed she had a private breeze which swirled around, cooling her. She was thin without the taut look of wiry people, and her printed voile dresses and flowered hats were as right for her as denim overalls for a farmer. She was our side's answer to the richest white woman in town.

*Introduces character and gives overall impression of her*

*Provides details of physical appearance*

Her skin was a rich black that would have peeled like a plum if snagged, but then no one would have thought of getting close enough to Mrs. Flowers to ruffle her dress, let alone snag her skin. She didn't encourage familiarity. She wore gloves too.

*Uses a simile (like a plum) to create image*

*Describes what other people think of her*

I don't think I ever saw Mrs. Flowers laugh, but she smiled often. A slow widening of her thin black lips to show even, small white teeth, then the slow effortless closing. When she chose to smile on me, I always wanted to thank her. The action was so graceful and inclusively benign.

*Uses vivid adjectives to portray character and action (smiling)*

*Shares personal experience with her*

1. In the opening sentence, what word does Angelou use to give an overall impression of Mrs. Flowers? What does this word suggest about her?

   _____

   _____

2. What do the details about Mrs. Flowers's physical appearance (her body and skin) suggest about her personality?

   _____

   _____

3. What do the details about Mrs. Flowers's clothing suggest about her personality?

   _____

   _____

4. How does the description of Mrs. Flowers's smile add to readers' understanding of her personality?

   _____

   _____

5. What does Angelou's personal experience with Mrs. Flowers suggest about her personality? Why is sharing this personal experience effective in characterizing Mrs. Flowers?

   _____

   _____

6. Review the three techniques of characterization that are explained at the beginning of this lesson. Which of these techniques does Angelou use in characterizing Mrs. Flowers? Support your answer with details from the excerpt.

   _____

   _____

   _____

   _____

# Your Assignment
## Write a Character Description

To complete this assignment, follow the five stages of the writing process: Prewrite, Draft, Revise, Edit and Proofread, and Publish and Present.

## ① Prewrite

Before you write, gather your thoughts and plan your description.

### Select a Subject to Write About

In choosing a subject—someone to describe—consider people who are distinctive or unique in some way. For example, do you know someone who wears outrageous or unique clothing? Who has unusual habits or mannerisms? Who speaks or acts in a particular way that reflects his or her personality? Consider friends, relatives, and acquaintances that you encounter in your daily routine. Also consider people from your past whom you might not see any longer but remember in detail.

List four people you might write about.

_____        _____

_____        _____

Consider each person and how well you think you can describe his or her personality through physical appearance, clothing, actions, and dialogue. Keep in mind that you will use these details about the person to reveal what he or she is like.

Choose one person to write about.

_____

### State Your Purpose and Identify Your Audience

For everything you write, you should consider why you are writing it and who will be reading it. Your purpose and audience will determine what you write and how you write it.

For example, in her autobiography, Maya Angelou's purpose was to reveal the personality of Mrs. Flowers to readers who do not know her. Another writer might describe a character who has made an impact on his or her life for the program of an awards celebration, and another writer might describe someone running for office for a newspaper or magazine article.

One student decided to write a character description of the man who delivers pizza to his house. The student had observed this man enough times to know about his appearance, actions, and speech and to have a sense of the man's personality. The student wrote this statement of purpose and audience:

> My purpose is to entertain my readers with a description of a quirky pizza delivery person.

Write a sentence stating your audience and purpose.

_____

_____

## Gather Your Information

Before you write, gather information about your subject. To do so, brainstorm about the qualities of the person you plan on describing. Organize your ideas using a chart like the one below.

The student writing about the pizza delivery man started by jotting down details about the delivery man's appearance, clothing, and so on. Then the student looked over the details and started to think about what they suggested about the delivery man. For instance, the fact that the delivery man's uniform was always neatly pressed and all his buttons were completely buttoned suggested that he took his job seriously. This was the impression the student had already formed of the man, as well. The student added these notes about personality to the chart.

To help you gather information, review the three characterization techniques described in the opening of this lesson. The first two involve *describing* and *showing* what the character is like. Think about the difference between the two: what you say outright versus what you suggest by what you say. Also think about whether you can work in details about what other people think or say about your character. The student writing about the delivery man included his mother's observation that the man was always "incredibly polite."

### Characterization Planning Chart

| Physical Appearance | Clothing | Actions | Speech |
|---|---|---|---|
| Stands really straight—like a soldier (1) | Full company uniform, including cap (3) | Carefully hands over pizza—like it's breakable or expensive (7) | Says "thank-you" when gets money—speaks quickly, crisply (8) |
| Short and stocky—maybe eats a lot of pizza! (2) | Red pants with yellow stripe down side—sharp crease (6) | Almost bows when gets money—respectful, official (9) | Says "thank-you" again— Calls Mom "M'am"— "incredibly polite" (10) |
| | Shirt pressed—all buttons buttoned (4) | Turns around quickly—like soldier (11) | |
| | Nametag on shirt (5) | Goes back to truck—moves quickly (12) | |
| | | Doesn't waste time—does job efficiently (13) | |

## Organize Your Information

Now that you have gathered your information, consider how best to organize it for your character description. Think about what details will create an initial impression of the person—for instance, his or her physical appearance and clothing. Then proceed with a description of what this person does and says; these details will

*Writing & Grammar*

likely fit together, as they all show the person in action. Remember that your goal in describing this person is to suggest what he or she is like.

Number the items in your Characterization Planning Chart in the order in which you will present them. Think carefully about what details should be presented together and what details should be added here and there. What do you want readers to think about this person?

The student writing about the pizza delivery man decided to start with a description of his physical appearance and clothing. All these details suggested that the man took his job very seriously, almost like a soldier. After having made this impression, the student worked in the details about the delivery man's actions and speech. The student concentrated on portraying this man as being official and soldierlike.

## ② Draft

For this assignment, write two or three paragraphs about your character. In the first paragraph, identify your character and state how or why you know this person, if that is relevant. Then describe the character's physical appearance and clothing. In the second paragraph (and third, if you like), describe the character's actions and speech.

In both paragraphs, stay focused on the personality that you want to reveal. Again, what do you want readers to understand about this person? Perhaps jot down some adjectives that capture his or her personality. For instance, the pizza delivery man's personality could be described using words such as *official, soldierlike, quick,* and *efficient.*

Also think some more about the difference between describing and showing. Good descriptive writing does both.

## ③ Revise

Be sure to allow yourself time after drafting to revise. During the Revise stage, evaluate the information you provided and the organization you followed. Have you described your character in enough detail? Will your audience get a sense of what this person is like?

Use the questions in column 1 of the Revision Checklist to identify areas that need improvement. Then, based on the evaluation, revise your draft. Use the suggestions in column 2 to fix the problems you have identified.

In revising your draft, you may decide to add, delete, or rearrange information to strengthen the argument you are making. Remember that your goal is to reveal someone's personality by describing his or her physical appearance, clothing, actions, and speech.

Read a printout of your draft, and mark your changes on the paper as you go. Think about whether your description paints a clear picture of your character.

## REVISION CHECKLIST

| Evaluate | Strengthen |
|---|---|
| ☐ Does your opening sentence or two identify the character and state how or why you know him or her? | Identify the subject of your character description, and state how or why you know this person, if that is relevant. |
| ☐ Does your first paragraph give the details of the character's physical appearance and dress? | Add the details from your planning chart about physical appearance and dress, following the order you decided. |
| ☐ Does the first paragraph create an overall impression of the character's personality? | Add more details or describe the character's appearance/clothing with specific adjectives to create an overall impression about personality. |
| ☐ Does the second (and third) paragraph provide details about the character's actions and speech? | Again, add the details from your planning chart, following the order you decided. |
| ☐ Does the second (and third) paragraph continue to develop the character's personality? | Add more details or describe the character's actions/speech with specific adjectives to further develop an impression about personality. |

## ④ Edit and Proofread

After you have revised your draft, edit it to check your spelling, punctuation, and grammar for errors. You may have found some of these kinds of errors already in the Revise stage, but read through it again to look for them more carefully now.

Also review your draft to look for ways to improve the descriptive power of your writing. Think of how you can bring your character to life for your readers, not only describing but showing what he or she is like. Review your use of adjectives, in particular, to make your descriptions more vivid. Review the Grammar & Style lesson for guidelines about using vivid adjectives.

Retype or rewrite your character description, making all of the changes you marked in editing. Then check the accuracy of this edited draft by doing a final proofread. Reading your work aloud is a good way to find any remaining errors.

Also reread your draft to make sure it meets the requirements of a character description, as listed in the Writing Rubric below. Check off each item that applies to your description.

Review the Original Student Draft and the Revised/Edited Student Draft to see the process one student followed in drafting and then revising and editing/proofreading his character description.

# Grammar & Style: Vivid Adjectives

Good descriptive writing uses vivid **adjectives** to capture specific details and to show or suggest qualities and traits. For instance, the description "His brown, weathered face" not only describes dark, wrinkled skin but also suggests the man is tough and rugged. Similarly, the description "Her *athletic* build" not only describes physical trimness and strength but also suggests the person is active and healthy.

In drafting, you may tend to use adjectives such as *good, nice*, and *important* that do not bring to mind vivid images. Review your draft for these overused and overly general adjectives, and use a thesaurus or dictionary to locate alternatives for them.

**Exercise:** For each physical feature below, write two adjectives that not only describe the physical feature but also suggests a personality trait. The first one is done for you.

1. **Skin**    _____ruddy_____        _____milky_____

2. **Eyes**    _____        _____

3. **Mouth**   _____        _____

4. **Hair**    _____        _____

5. **Height**  _____        _____

6. **Voice**   _____        _____

Now go back to your revised draft and see if you can replace any overused, general adjectives with more vivid, specific adjectives.

 WRITING RUBRIC

An effective character description has these qualities:
- ❑ In the first sentence or two, identifies the character and how or why the writer knows him or her
- ❑ Describes the character's physical appearance and clothing and creates a general impression of his or her personality
- ❑ Describes the character's actions and speech and further develops an impression of his or her personality
- ❑ Both describes and shows what the character is like using vivid adjectives
- ❑ Uses correct punctuation, grammar, spelling, and vocabulary

Did you check off each item? If not, consider making additional changes to your character description.

**Original Student Draft**

   The pizza delivery man arrived at the door, rang the bell, and stood there. He was short and stocky, like someone who eats a lot of pizza! He wore the full company uniform, right down to the small red cap on his head. His red shirt was pressed, and all the buttons were buttoned. His nametag was pinned to the pocket on his shirt. His red pants had a yellow stripe down the side and were pressed with a sharp crease.

   He handed over the pizza as if he were handing over something breakable or expensive. He said "Thank-you" quickly when I gave him the money. When Mom reached over and gave him a tip, he said "Thank-you, M'am" and almost seemed to bow. Mom always says he's really polite.

   The pizza delivery man turned around quickly and headed out the door. We watched him walk quickly back to his truck and climb in. He was quick and efficient. Then he was off again, delivering another pizza!

**Revised/Edited Student Draft**

   The pizza delivery man arrived at the door, rang the bell, and stood there**, stiff and straight as a soldier.** He was short and stocky, like someone who eats a lot of pizza! He ~~wore~~ **looked very official in** the full company uniform, right down to the small red cap on his head. His red shirt was **neatly** pressed, and all the buttons were **carefully** buttoned. His nametag**, which said SARGENT,** was pinned **squarely** to the pocket on his shirt. His red pants had a yellow stripe down the side and were pressed with a **razor-**sharp crease.

   **He SARGENT** handed over the pizza as if he were handing over ~~something breakable or expensive~~ **an expensive glass platter.** He said "Thank-you" ~~quickly~~ **crisply** when I gave him the money. When Mom reached over and gave him a tip, he said "Thank-you, M'am" and almost seemed to bow. Mom always says he's ~~really~~ **incredibly** polite.

   ~~The pizza delivery man~~ **SARGENT** turned around ~~quickly~~ **abruptly** and headed out the door. We watched him walk ~~quickly~~ **briskly** back to his truck and climb in. ~~He was quick and efficient.~~ Then he was off again, ~~delivering another pizza~~ **on to his next mission**!

Adds descriptive details to help create impression of personality

Makes up silly name, given humorous purpose

Uses more specific adjective

Describes action by creating image

Replaces general adjectives with more specific ones

Deletes unnecessary sentence

Leaves readers with final image

## ⑤ Publish and Present

- Draw a sketch of the person you have described. Then display your character description and sketch on a bulletin board with the descriptions and sketches your classmates have created.
- Suppose that the person you described is going to be a character in a short story or novel. Write a short summary of what the story or novel will be about, including the actions your character will perform and the situations he or she will be involved in.

## ARGUMENTATIVE WRITING
# Persuade Using Examples

**Persuasion** is the ability to change or influence the way others think or feel about a particular issue or idea. Every day, you are the intended audience of persuasive appeals in the forms of print and television advertisements, speeches, articles, billboards, television programs, and even T-shirts. Every day, you also likely use persuasion when you try to convince parents, friends, teachers, and others of your viewpoints.

    An **argumentative essay** uses persuasion to convince others of a particular point of view, or **thesis statement.** To convince requires providing information that proves or supports that thesis or argument. Using examples to demonstrate the truth or reason behind a point of view is an effective way to persuade readers.

## Learn from a Literary Model

Read the passage below from "Indian Cattle," an informational text by Eugene Rachlis, on pages 280–284 of your textbook. Note how Rachlis gives examples to convince readers of the importance of the buffalo to the Plains Indians. Note, too, that this passage has been excerpted, or used in parts, to demonstrate the use of examples. For the complete text, go to your textbook.

### from **Indian Cattle, by Eugene Rachlis**

    Of all the things the horse put within reach of the Plains Indians, none was as important as the buffalo. The big, ugly, shaggy animal represented life itself.…

*States point of view, or thesis*

    Even as a child the Indian knew the importance of buffalo. Before they had teeth, children sucked bits of buffalo meat. As they grew older, they learned to know that the meat from the cow made better eating than that from the bull. Buffalo tongue was a special treat, and served as a sacred food in many ceremonies. Great feasts followed successful hunts. Large pieces of the newly-killed buffalo were roasted over an open fire, and handed out to feed all who were hungry.…

*Writes topic sentence that supports thesis: children know importance of buffalo*

*Provides examples to support topic sentence*

    It was not surprising that the Indians held tribal celebrations when they feasted on fresh buffalo meat. For, during most of the year, the Plains Indians ate preserved meat, which had been saved for use during the long periods when fresh meat was impossible to find.… Food was only one of the many things the buffalo contributed to the Plains Indians. Buffalo skin was used in innumerable ways. The hides of the buffalo killed in winter were covered with heavy fur. From these winter hides the Indians made mittens, caps, moccasins, and robes, which could be used as blankets or as a kind of overcoat.

*Continues with topic of food/celebrations*

*Transition sentence makes shift to new topic: uses of buffalo skin*

*Provides more examples of use of buffalo skin*

But the Indians had use for more than the skin. The bones of the buffalo were used as tools for farming; the sinews were used as thread and, when twisted, made excellent bowstrings; the horns were used as spoons, ladles, and cups; the stomach was cleaned and made into a bag for carrying food or water; sometimes it served as a cooking pot. The dung of the buffalo—called "buffalo chips"—was used as fuel....

*Transition/topic sentence makes shift to new topic: more uses*

*Provides more examples*

1. The first paragraph contains the thesis statement, or the point of view that will be proven in this informational text. What thesis does Rachlis, the author, plan to prove?

   _____

2. What is the topic sentence of the second paragraph? How does it relate back to and support the thesis statement?

   _____

3. In paragraph 2, what examples does Rachlis provide to support the topic sentence?

   _____

4. Paragraph 3 continues discussing the celebrations that involved having fresh buffalo meat. Then the discussion shifts to discussing uses of the buffalo other than for food. What sentence points out this shift, or transition?

   _____

5. After the transition in paragraph 3, what examples of other uses of the buffalo does the author give?

   _____

6. The topic sentence of paragraph 4 indicates another transition, or shift in topic. What is the topic of this paragraph? What examples are given to support it?

   _____

## Your Assignment
### Write an Argumentative Essay Using Examples

To complete this assignment, follow the five stages of the writing process: Prewrite, Draft, Revise, Edit and Proofread, and Publish and Present.

## ① Prewrite

Before you write, gather your thoughts and plan your argumentative essay.

## Select a Subject to Write About

In choosing a subject, consider opinions that you have and especially opinions that you would feel compelled to argue with someone about. Maybe you have a strong opinion about a professional athlete or sports team, good or bad. Maybe you feel strongly about your favorite book, movie, pet, or vacation spot. Maybe there is an issue in your school, neighborhood, or community that you are strongly for or against.

On the lines below, list four subjects and what opinion you have about each one.

_____

_____

_____

_____

Now think about why you have these opinions. How did you come to form each opinion? What makes you think your opinion is right or valid? Could you convince others to agree with your opinion?

Many people develop strong opinions about subjects of importance to them, ranging from sports teams to political issues. Some people's strongest views come from things they have experienced. For example, one student felt strongly that moving frequently provided opportunities to see new places and meet new people. This opinion was based on her own experiences as a so-called army brat: someone whose mother or father is in the military and thus has to move often. This student believed that she could use her experiences of moving around the world to convince people of her opinion.

Choose one subject/opinion, and write it here.

_____

_____

## State Your Purpose and Identify Your Audience

For everything you write, you should consider why you are writing it and who will be reading it. Your purpose and audience will determine what you write and how you write it.

For example, if you were trying to convince a friend not to be afraid of moving, you might share your own positive experiences with this subject. Using examples from your own life would help you make a convincing case for your point of view. However, if you were trying to convince your parents not to move, you might use examples from teachers and counselors about the difficulties of uprooting students from their school and friends. Examples from these professionals would lend strong support to your opinion.

The student with a strong opinion about the benefits of moving wrote this statement of purpose and audience:

I am writing about how moving benefits the children of military personnel for an editorial in the U.S. Army newsletter.

State your purpose and audience on the lines below.

_____

_____

## Gather Your Information

Before you write, gather information about your subject. Start by brainstorming three or four reasons you can provide to support your opinion. Then for each reason, jot down specific examples that support or prove that point. Record all this information in a web like the one below.

The student writing about the benefits of moving brainstormed four reasons, or benefits. Then she jotted down examples from her own life to support those reasons. Based on her purpose and audience, she felt that her firsthand experiences as an army brat would be convincing. She recorded her ideas in the following Brainstorming Web.

### Brainstorming Web

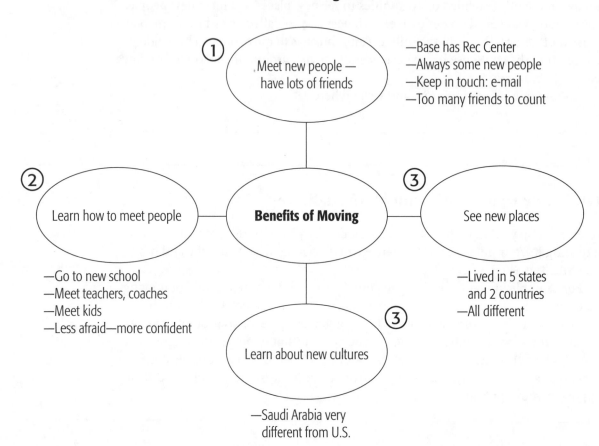

① Meet new people — have lots of friends
—Base has Rec Center
—Always some new people
—Keep in touch: e-mail
—Too many friends to count

② Learn how to meet people
—Go to new school
—Meet teachers, coaches
—Meet kids
—Less afraid—more confident

**Benefits of Moving**

③ See new places
—Lived in 5 states and 2 countries
—All different

③ Learn about new cultures
—Saudi Arabia very different from U.S.

*Writing & Grammar*

## Organize Your Information

Now that you have gathered your information, consider how best to organize it for your argumentative essay.

Review the reasons and examples in your Brainstorming Web, and think about which ones best support the opinion you are stating. Also think about whether any reasons are similar enough to be combined or whether any are off the subject and should be dropped.

Choose three reasons to include in your essay. Then number them in the order in which you will present them. In argumentative writing, it is common to present the reasons in order from weakest to strongest. That way, you build a strong case to convince your readers.

The student writing about moving reviewed her Brainstorming Web and realized that two of her reasons could be combined. The "See new places" and "Learn about new cultures" items could be combined in an item "Learn about new places and cultures." The student felt this item was her strongest reason in support of moving, so she numbered it 3. She thought that "Learn how to meet people" should follow "Meet new people—have lots of friends," so she numbered them 2 and 1, respectively.

## Write a Thesis Statement

The point of view you will present in your argumentative essay will be your **thesis statement,** or the main idea you will argue. Before writing your thesis, go back and review your statement of purpose and audience. Now that you have gathered and organized information about your subject, you likely have a more specific idea about which to write. That specific idea should be your thesis statement.

The student who believed in the benefits of moving wrote this thesis statement:

Moving benefits the children of military personnel in several ways.

Write your thesis statement here.

_____

_____

## ② Draft

In drafting, follow the three-part structure of an essay: introduction, body, and conclusion.

## Introduction

Your first paragraph, the **introduction,** should identify your subject and grab your readers' attention. Consider what will get readers interested and make them want to read more. Common types of attention-getters include the following:
- an interesting fact or statistic about the subject
- a short story about a personal experience with the subject (whether your or someone else's experience)

- a quotation or statement from someone who knows about the subject
- a description or definition of the subject

After getting readers' attention, tell them what your essay will be about by giving them your thesis statement.

## Body

In the **body** of your essay, develop the information you gathered and organized in the Prewrite stage. Use this information to support or prove the thesis you stated in your introduction.

For each reason in your Brainstorming Web, write a sentence stating the point you want to make. For instance, for the essay about moving, the student wrote this sentence about the "Learn how to meet people" reason:

Moving a lot helps you learn how to meet people.

Use this sentence as the **topic sentence** for a paragraph about this reason. Write additional sentences for the paragraph using the examples you listed for each reason. Each additional sentence should somehow prove or support the reason stated in the topic sentence.

The body of your essay should have three paragraphs like this, in which you state a reason and then support it with examples. Together, these body paragraphs should prove or support the thesis you stated in your introduction. Again, think of building a case to convince your readers of your opinion.

## Conclusion

The last paragraph of your essay, the **conclusion,** should restate your thesis and provide a sense of closure. What final thought or idea do you want your readers to have?

## ③ Revise

Be sure to allow yourself time after drafting to revise. During the Revise stage, evaluate the information you provided and the organization you followed. Have you built a strong case for your opinion? Will your audience be persuaded to agree with you?

Use the questions in column 1 of the Revision Checklist to identify areas that need improvement. Then, based on the evaluation, revise your draft. Use the suggestions in column 2 to fix the problems you have identified.

In revising your draft, you may decide to add, delete, or rearrange information to strengthen the argument you are making. Remember that your goal is to persuade your audience to accept your point of view. Presenting information in a clear, logical manner is especially important in writing an argumentative essay.

Read a printout of your draft, and mark your changes on the paper as you go. Think about whether your essay presents a clear opinion and then convinces readers to agree with it.

## REVISION CHECKLIST

| Evaluate | Strengthen |
|---|---|
| ❏ Do you identify your subject and get readers' attention in your introduction? | Clarify your subject and review the suggestions for ways to get readers' attention. |
| ❏ Do you state your thesis in the introduction? | Clearly state your thesis so readers will know the opinion you plan to prove in your essay. |
| ❏ Does each body paragraph have a strong topic sentence followed by several supporting examples? | Add or revise the topic sentence, stating the main idea of the paragraph, and then support that idea with several sentences that provide clear examples. |
| ❏ Do your body paragraphs build a case in support of your thesis, leading up to your most important reason? | Review the order in which you present the reasons for your opinion, and rearrange them if needed. |
| ❏ Does your conclusion restate your thesis and create a sense of closure? | Add a restated version of your thesis, along with the final idea or thought you would like readers to have. |

## ④ Edit and Proofread

After you have revised your draft, edit it to check your spelling, punctuation, and grammar for errors. You may have found some of these kinds of errors already in revising your draft, but read through it again to look for them more carefully.

Also review your draft to look for ways to improve the persuasive power of your writing. Think of how you can convince readers to accept your opinion. One way to do that is to make clear connections between your ideas using transitional words, phrases, and sentences. Review the Grammar & Style lesson for guidelines about using transitions.

Retype or rewrite your argumentative essay, making all of the changes you marked in editing. Then check the accuracy of this edited draft by doing a final proofread. Having a classmate read your essay is a good way to find any remaining errors.

Also reread your draft to make sure it meets the requirements of an argumentative essay using examples, as listed in the Writing Rubric below. Check off each item that applies to your essay.

Review the Original Student Draft and the Revised/Edited Student Draft to see the process one student followed in drafting and then revising and editing/proofreading her argumentative essay.

A successful argumentative essay has these qualities:
- ❏ Identifies the subject and gets readers' attention in the introduction
- ❏ Presents a strong thesis statement in the introduction
- ❏ Has body paragraphs that begin with a topic sentence and then support it with examples
- ❏ Is organized to build a strong case and prove the thesis
- ❏ Has a conclusion that restates the thesis and provides a final thought
- ❏ Uses transitional words, phrases, and sentences to link ideas
- ❏ Uses correct punctuation, grammar, spelling, and vocabulary

Did you check off each item? If not, consider making additional changes to your argumentative essay.

## Original Student Draft

I have lived my entire life on military bases around the country and around the world. Some people say this is no way for a kid to grow up, but I say it's great! Moving benefits the children of military personnel in several ways.

One benefit of moving frequently is that you meet a lot of people and make a lot of friends. Most U.S. Army bases have a recreation center for families, so it's easy to meet new kids quickly. There are always new kids at military bases. We keep in touch mostly through e-mail. Just today, I received three e-mails from old friends. I once started listing all the friends I've made at different bases, but there were too many to count.

Moving a lot makes you learn how to meet people. Every time I've moved, I've had to go to a new school and introduce myself to new teachers and coaches. I've had to meet new kids and find ways of fitting in and making friends. With all this practice, I've become less afraid and more confident about meeting people. I really enjoy it!

Learning about different places and cultures is a benefit of moving frequently. I have lived in five states and two countries, and they have all been really different. For example, I have experienced firsthand Alaska, Louisiana, Iowa, California, and New Hampshire. I have lived in Saudi Arabia, where life is totally different from in the United States.

Although most kids hate the thought of leaving their homes and friends, moving is good for them in many ways.

# Grammar & Style: Transitions

**Transitions** are words, phrases, and sentences that show readers the links between ideas. Common single-word transitions include *but, next, and, also, although,* and *however.* Common transitional phrases include *in addition, for example, for instance,* and *in conclusion.*

The transition often comes at the beginning of the sentence, as shown in the first example below. However, a transition can also be used in the middle or at the end of a sentence, as in the second and third examples:

We were supposed to complete the project by Friday. *However,* we didn't realize how much work would be involved.

We were supposed to complete the project by Friday. We didn't realize, *however,* how much work would be involved.

We were supposed to complete the project by Friday. We didn't realize how much work would be involved, *however.*

Notice that in all the examples, the transition word is set off from the rest of the sentence by one or two commas.

In "Indian Cattle," the author, Eugene Rachlis, uses complete sentences as transitions to indicate shifts in topic within and between paragraphs. For instance, midway through the paragraph about the Plains Indians using the meat from the buffalo, Rachlis adds this transitional sentence to shift the topic to using the skin of the buffalo:

Food was only one of the many things the buffalo contributed to the Plains Indians. Buffalo skin was used in innumerable ways.

Transition sentences are best used between paragraphs of an essay to indicate major shifts in the topic.

**Exercise:** In each blank, write a transition word or phrase to link the sentences, forming one or two sentences. Change the capitalization and punctuation around the transition, as needed.

1. There are many places I would like to visit someday. _____ I would like to go to China.

2. It would be helpful to speak Chinese. _____ I only know how to speak Spanish.

3. I have been to Mexico. _____ I have been to Canada.

4. When I'm a senior in high school, my class will take a trip to Washington, DC. That seems like a long time away. _____.

Now review your draft to see if the links between your sentences and paragraphs are clear. Where the link is not clear, add a transition to make a smooth connection.

**Revised/Edited Student Draft**

**As an "army brat,"** I have lived my entire life on military bases around the country and around the world. Some people say this is no way for a kid to grow up, but I say it's great! Moving benefits the children of military personnel in several ways.

One benefit of moving frequently is that you meet a lot of people and make a lot of friends. Most U.S. Army bases have a recreation center for families, so it's easy to meet new kids quickly. There are always new kids at military bases. **I once started listing all the friends I've made at different bases, but there were too many to count.** We keep in touch mostly through e-mail. **For example,** ~~J~~just today, I received three e-mails from old friends. ~~I once started listing all the friends I've made at different bases, but there were too many to count.~~

**In addition,** ~~M~~moving a lot makes you learn how to meet people. Every time I've moved, I've had to go to a new school and introduce myself to new teachers and coaches. I've **also** had to meet new kids and find ways of fitting in and making friends. With all this practice, I've become less afraid and more confident about meeting people. I really enjoy it!

Learning about different places and cultures is **a another** benefit of moving frequently. I have lived in five states and two countries, and they have all been really different. For example, I have experienced firsthand **the cold of** Alaska, **the heat of** Louisiana, **the farmlands of** Iowa, **the beaches of** California, and **the mountains of** New Hampshire. I have **also** lived in Saudi Arabia, where life is totally different from in the United States.

Although most kids hate the thought of leaving their homes and friends, moving is good for them in many ways. **Parents of "army brats" shouldn't worry about moving their children too much. It's actually good for them!**

*Adds detail to establish authority on topic and get readers' attention*

*States thesis*

*Topic sentence states first reason*

*Gives examples of meeting people*

*Moves sentence for better organization*

*Adds transition*

*Adds transition*

*Topic sentence states second reason*

*Adds transition*

*Adds transition*

*Topic sentence states third reason*

*Adds details to show differences*

*Adds transition*

*Adds closing thought for specific audience*

## ⑤ Publish and Present

- Share your essay with your intended audience, and get feedback from your reader or readers. Were they persuaded to accept your point of view? Why or why not?
- One good way to gather information for an argumentative essay is to think about the *counterargument,* or the opinion opposite your own. Knowing the examples and other support details an opponent would use to prove his or her argument can help you prepare your argument. Write a paragraph stating the counterargument to your opinion and two or three reasons supporting that counterargument. Do you counter or disprove those reasons in your essay? If not, think about revising your work.

## INFORMATIVE WRITING
# Explain Using Details

By this time in your schooling, you have probably written several paragraphs or papers in which you have *explained* something. You might have had to explain the causes of the Civil War, the process of photosynthesis, or the use of light in a Rembrandt painting.

Writing that explains or informs is called **informative writing.** A good **informative essay** states a main idea, or **thesis,** and then provides details that help readers understand the subject. These details may come in the form of actions, descriptions, and statements of facts—all designed to help readers understand.

## Learn from a Literary Model

Read the following excerpt from "Immigrant Kids," an essay by Russell Freedman, on pages 354–356 in your textbook. In this passage, Freedman quotes Edward Corsi, former U.S. Commissioner of Immigration, who was ten years old when he sailed into New York Harbor after emigrating from Italy. Notice how Corsi uses a variety of details to explain his first impression of the United States.

### from **Immigrant Kids, by Russell Freedman**

My first impressions of the New World will always remain etched in my memory, particularly that hazy October morning when I first saw Ellis Island. The steamer *Florida,* fourteen days out of Naples, filled to capacity with 1,600 natives of Italy, had weathered one of the worst storms in our captain's memory; and glad we were, both children and grown-ups, to leave the open sea and come at last through the Narrows into the Bay.

*Identifies subject*

*Gives facts about ship and voyage*

My mother, my stepfather, my brother Giuseppe, and my two sisters, Liberta and Helvetia, all of us together, happy that we had come through the storm safely, clustered on the foredeck for fear of separation and looked with wonder on this miraculous land of our dreams.

*Identifies family members*

*Describes emotions*

Giuseppe and I held tightly to Stepfather's hands, while Liberta and Helvetia clung to Mother. Passengers all about us were crowding against the rail. Jabbered conversation, sharp cries, laughs and cheers—a steadily rising din filled the air. Mothers and fathers lifted up babies so that they too could see, off to the left, the Statue of Liberty….

*Describes action*

*Adds details of sounds*

Finally the *Florida* veered to the left, turning northward into the Hudson River and now the incredible buildings of lower Manhattan came very close to us.

*Describes action*
*Describes reaction*

The officers of the ship…went striding up and down the decks shouting orders and directions and driving the immigrants before them. Scowling and gesturing, they pushed and pulled the passengers, herding us into separate groups as though we were animals. A few moments later we came to our dock, and the long journey was over.

*Describes action*

*Suggests tension and fear*

*Comes to logical close*

1. What is the subject of this essay?

_____

_____

2. State two factual details about the ship and the voyage.

_____

_____

3. What details does the author of this passage give about his family?

_____

_____

4. Why might the author have given the names of his brother and sisters? What effect might knowing these names have on the reader?

_____

_____

5. In the second paragraph, what emotions does the author mention?

_____

_____

6. What actions does the author describe in paragraphs 3, 4, and 5?

_____

_____

7. In the last paragraph, the officers of the ship are described as "striding up and down the decks shouting orders and directions and driving the immigrants before them." What do these details add to the author's description of his experience?

_____

_____

8. How do you feel at the end of the essay? What emotion does the ending create in you?

_____

_____

# Your Assignment
## Write an Explanatory Essay Using Details

To complete this assignment, follow the five stages of the writing process: Prewrite, Draft, Revise, Edit and Proofread, and Publish and Present.

# ① Prewrite

Before you write, gather your thoughts and plan your essay.

## Select a Subject to Write About

In choosing a subject, consider things related to you personally, such as your favorite activities, books, and movies; your family and friends; and your goals and ambitions. Also consider explaining things that go beyond you, such as the latest video game, cell phone, or computer; the concert tour of a musician or musical group; and issues in your school or community.

On the lines below, list four subjects you might write about.

_____        _____

_____        _____

Now think about what details you would have to provide to explain each subject to someone. For example, if one of your favorite activities is to go to the local carnival, you can draw on several types of details for your essay. Among these would be the sights, sounds, and smells of the rides, games, and foods.

Consider each subject and the details you could use to explain it. Then choose one subject and write it down here.

_____

## State Your Purpose and Identify Your Audience

For everything you write, you should consider why you are writing it and who will be reading it. Your purpose and audience will determine what you write and how you write it.

For example, if you were writing a technical explanation of a carnival for someone who is unfamiliar with this type of amusement, you would have to provide factual details such as the layout, the numbers of rides and events, the numbers of people working and attending the carnival, and so on. But if you were giving your impression of a carnival for a friend, the details would be more observational and personal. For this type of essay, you would write a statement of purpose and audience like this:

I am explaining to a friend why I like the local carnival.

Write a statement identifying your purpose and audience.

_____

## Gather Your Information

Before you write, gather information about your subject. Brainstorm about the different types of details you can use to explain your subject. Start with general categories of details, such as "Facts," "Actions," "Senses," and "Emotions." Then fill in specific details in each category. Record your information in a chart like the one below.

The student writing about the carnival started by recording the factual details in column 1 and then the actions in column 2. Recording the actions, in particular, made her think of details to add in the "Senses" and "Emotions" columns. For instance, the action of "Going on rides" made her think of the emotions she feels when she rides the roller coaster. Similarly, the action of "Eating" made her think of the smells of foods that fill the air at the carnival.

### Explanation Planning Chart

| Facts | Actions | Senses | Emotions |
|---|---|---|---|
| Annual carnival—held at fairgrounds every June by Fire Department ① | Going on rides—especially roller coaster ⑨ | Sounds—kids squealing, workers yelling, clacking of rides, music from live band ④ | Going on roller coaster—both fear and excitement ⑩ |
| People of all ages attend—have favorite things ② | Playing games of chance—pitching balls, tossing rings, "strong man" hammer Winning prizes ⑦ | Smells—different smells everywhere from rides and food ⑤ | Playing games of chance—everyone eager for player, happy when someone wins ⑧ |
| | Eating—every teen's favorites ⑥ | Sights—activity everywhere, constant motion ③ | |

## Organize Your Information

Now that you have gathered your information, consider how best to organize it. Keep in mind that your purpose is to explain your subject. What type of organization would best fit this purpose?

If you are explaining some kind of event or experience, it makes sense to organize the actions in the order in which they happened; then add the other details where they seem to fit within the actions. The story told by the immigrant boy in the Literary Model follows this type of **chronological organization.** If you are writing about a place, a process, or a kind of technology, you might want to focus on the facts and then work in the other details.

The student writing about her love of carnivals decided to start her essay with the facts. Then she decided to explain the atmosphere of the carnival by describing the different sensory details: sights, sounds, and smells. Finally, the student planned

*Writing & Grammar*

to write about the actions at the carnival. She decided to write about going on the rides last, because that action seemed the most exciting of the three.

Number the details in your Explanation Planning Chart in the order in which you will write about them. See the student example for a model.

## Write Your Thesis Statement

Your **thesis statement** should identify your subject and tell readers what you plan to say about it. You should be able to state this main idea in a single sentence.

To write your thesis, work from the statement of purpose and audience that you wrote earlier. Now that you have gathered and organized information about your subject, you probably have a more specific idea of what you want to say in your essay.

The student who chose to explain carnivals wrote this thesis statement:

The local carnival provides all the atmosphere and action that makes carnivals fun for people of all ages.

Write your thesis statement here.

_____

_____

## ② Draft

In drafting, follow the three-part structure of an essay: introduction, body, and conclusion.

## Introduction

Your **introduction,** or first paragraph, should identify your subject and capture your readers' attention. Think about how you can get your readers interested and make them want to read more. Depending on what best fits your subject, you might try one of these attention-getters:

- Start with an interesting fact or statistic about the subject.
- Share a short story about a personal experience with the subject (whether your or someone else's experience).
- Give a quotation or statement from someone who knows about the subject.
- Offer a description or definition of the subject.

Your introduction should also present your thesis statement, telling readers the main idea of your essay.

## Body

The **body** of your essay should present the information you gathered and organized in the Prewrite stage. Use this information to support or prove the thesis you stated in your introduction.

Review your Explanation Planning Chart and the order in which you decided to present the information. Identify each main point in your explanation, and write one paragraph about each point.

Start by writing a sentence about each main point. For instance, the student writing about carnivals wrote this sentence about the atmosphere:

The atmosphere of the carnival is created by a mixture of sights, sounds, and smells.

Use this sentence as the **topic sentence** for a paragraph about this idea. Write additional sentences for the paragraph using the details you listed in your planning chart. Each additional sentence should somehow prove or support the idea stated in the topic sentence.

The body of your essay should have three or four paragraphs like this, in which you state and then prove or support an idea with details. And each paragraph you write should prove or support the thesis you stated in your introduction. Remember that your purpose is to explain your subject.

## Conclusion

The **conclusion** of your essay should be a short paragraph that does two things: restate your thesis and give readers a sense of finality or closure. Consider what final thought or idea you want your readers to have.

## ③ Revise

Allow yourself enough time after drafting to revise your work. During the Revise stage, evaluate the information you provided and the organization you followed. Have you provided a good explanation of your subject? Will your audience understand your subject after reading your essay?

Use the questions in column 1 of the Revision Checklist to identify areas that need improvement. Then, based on the evaluation, revise your draft. Use the suggestions in column 2 to fix the problems you have identified.

In revising your draft, you may decide to add, delete, or rearrange information to strengthen the argument you are making. Again, remember that your goal is to explain your subject using details. Think carefully about the types of details you provide and the order in which you provide them.

Read a printout of your draft, and mark your changes on the paper as you go. Think about whether your essay presents a clear explanation that readers will understand.

*Writing & Grammar*

## REVISION CHECKLIST

| Evaluate | Strengthen |
|---|---|
| ❏ Does your introduction identify your subject and get readers' attention? | Clarify your subject and review the suggestions for ways to get readers' attention. |
| ❏ Do you state your thesis in the introduction? | Clearly state your thesis so readers will understand the main idea you plan to prove or support in your essay. |
| ❏ Does each body paragraph have a strong topic sentence followed by several sentences that provide supporting details? | Add or revise the topic sentence, stating the main idea of the paragraph, and then support that idea with several sentences containing specific details. |
| ❏ Are your body paragraphs organized in a way that will help readers understand your subject? | Review the order in which you present the supporting points and details, and rearrange them if needed. |
| ❏ Does your conclusion restate your thesis and give readers a sense of finality or closure? | Add a restated version of your thesis, along with the final idea or thought you would like readers to have. |

## ④ Edit and Proofread

After you have revised your draft, edit it to check your spelling, punctuation, and grammar for errors. Even though you may have found some of these kinds of errors already in revising your draft, you should read through it again to look for errors more carefully.

Also review your draft to look for ways to improve the explanatory power of your writing. Think of how you can best explain your subject to your readers. What information do they need? In what order will it make most sense? In addition, review your use of pronouns for both accuracy and clarity. Review the Grammar & Style lesson for guidelines about using pronouns.

Retype or rewrite your informative essay, making all of the changes you marked in editing. Then check the accuracy of this edited draft by doing a final proofread. Having a classmate read your essay is a good way to find any remaining errors.

Also reread your draft to make sure it meets the requirements of an informative essay using details, as listed in the Writing Rubric on page 46. Check off each item that applies to your essay.

Review the Original Student Draft and the Revised/Edited Student Draft to see the process one student followed in drafting and then revising and editing/proofreading her informative essay.

A successful informative essay has these qualities:
- ❏ Identifies the subject and gets readers' attention in the introduction
- ❏ Presents a strong thesis statement in the introduction
- ❏ Has body paragraphs that each begin with a topic sentence and then support it with details
- ❏ Is organized to provide a clear explanation and support the thesis
- ❏ Has a conclusion that restates the thesis and provides a final thought
- ❏ Uses pronouns correctly and clearly
- ❏ Uses correct punctuation, grammar, spelling, and vocabulary

Did you check off each item? If not, consider making additional changes to your informative essay.

## Original Student Draft

Some of my favorite memories from childhood are about going to carnivals. Whether the carnival was big or small, I loved everything about it. The local carnival provides all the atmosphere and action that makes carnivals fun for people of all ages.

The Georgetown Fire Department puts on the carnival at the fairgrounds every June. People of all ages attend, and we all have our favorite things.

The atmosphere of the carnival is created by a mixture of sights, sounds, and smells. Something is happening everywhere; there is constant activity. The carnival is also full of different sounds, such as kids squealing, workers yelling, rides clacking, and music playing. There are different smells, too, from both the rides and the food.

Being outdoors and having fun makes you hungry. All kinds of food are available at the carnival. You have a choice of every teenager's favorites.

Playing games of chance is another kind of fun at the carnival. You can try your luck at everything from pitching baseballs and tossing rings to slamming down the "strong man" hammer. All the people watching are eager for the player to win and happy when they get a prize.

The best part of the carnival is the rides. Little kids have their favorite rides, and big kids have theirs. The king of all carnival rides, of course, is the roller coaster. I start to get excited even before the ride starts, as I'm being strapped into the car. Then once the ride starts, I love cruising around the curves and being jarred from side to side. I especially love plunging down the hills and then climbing back to the top. The thrill of riding the roller coaster is a combination of fear and excitement.

The local carnival has everything you need to have fun.

# Grammar & Style: Pronouns

**Pronouns** are words that can be substituted for nouns, mostly to avoid having to repeat the same nouns again and again. Commonly used pronouns include *he, she, it, they, you,* and *I.*

To use a pronoun correctly, the noun it replaces must be clearly identified. That noun, called the **referent,** must be stated before the pronoun is used for the meaning to be clear.

Many writers use the pronouns *you/your* and *they/their* without having a referent. Look at these examples:

The student finished their test early and turned it in.

Most students know you should take all the time that's allowed for a test.

In the first example, the referent *student* is singular, so the pronoun must be singular, too. The pronoun *their* should be replaced by *his or her,* using both pronouns together.

In the second example, the referent *students* is plural, so the pronoun must also be plural. The pronoun *you* should be replaced by *they.*

The second example also illustrates the common error of using the pronoun *you* to refer to people in general. Many writers direct their message to an unknown *you,* as in this example:

*You* should start planning for college during *your* second or third year of high school.

Readers will likely understand that the *you* means *students,* but the pronoun has no referent. To correct this sentence, add the referent and then use the correct pronoun:

*Students* should start planning for college during *their* second or third year of high school.

**Exercise:** Fix the error or errors in pronoun use in each of the following sentences. Add the referent and/or substitute the correct pronoun, as needed.

1. I like skiing because it gives you a chance to be outdoors in winter.

2. You do all your work on computers in some classes.

3. In some countries, you only go to school through the eighth grade.

4. The server in that restaurant wasn't very good at their job.

Now go back to your revised draft and check your use of pronouns. Add referents and substitute pronouns where necessary for accuracy and clarity.

## Revised/Edited Student Draft

Some of my favorite memories from childhood are about going to carnivals. Whether the carnival was big or small, I loved everything about it. The local carnival provides all the atmosphere and action that makes carnivals fun for people of all ages.

**The local carnival is held the same time and place each year.**
The Georgetown Fire Department puts on the carnival at the fairgrounds

Identifies subject

Starts with personal story

Presents thesis statement

Adds topic sentence

every June. People of all ages attend, and **we they** all have **our their** favorite things.

The atmosphere of the carnival is created by a mixture of sights, sounds, and smells. Something is happening everywhere; there is constant activity. The carnival is also full of different sounds, such as kids squealing **in delight,** workers yelling **to attract customers,** rides clacking **and spinning with motion,** and music playing **from a live band.** There are different smells, too, from both the rides and the food.

~~Being outdoors and having fun makes you hungry.~~ All kinds of food are available at the carnival. ~~You have a choice of~~ **The choices include** every teenager's favorites**: hot dogs, hamburgers, french fries, pizza, popcorn, and cotton candy. Being outdoors and having fun makes everyone hungry**.

Playing games of chance is another kind of fun at the carnival. ~~You~~ **People** can try **your their** luck at everything from pitching baseballs and tossing rings to slamming down the "strong man" hammer. All the people watching are eager for the player to win and happy when ~~they~~ **he or she** get**s** a prize, **like a stuffed animal.**

The best part of the carnival is the rides. Little kids have their favorite rides, and big kids have theirs. The king of all carnival rides, of course, is the roller coaster. I start to get excited even before the ride starts, as I'm being strapped into the car. Then once the ride starts, I love cruising around the curves and being jarred from side to side. I especially love plunging down the hills and then climbing back to the top**, only to plunge down again.** The thrill of riding the roller coaster is a combination of fear and excitement.

The local carnival has everything ~~you~~ **anyone** need**s** to have fun. **Everyone is a kid again at the carnival!**

*Presents facts*
*Corrects pronoun errors*
*Topic sentence states main idea of paragraph: atmosphere*
*Adds more details*

*Topic sentence states topic: food*
*Corrects pronoun error*
*Adds more details*
*Moves sentence for better organization*
*Topic sentence states main idea of paragraph: games*
*Corrects pronoun errors*
*Adds detail*
*Topic sentence states main idea of paragraph: rides*

*Adds detail*

*Corrects pronoun error*
*Adds final thought*

# ⑤ Publish and Present

- Present an oral reading of your essay for your class. Think about where you might pause, slow down or speed up, emphasize certain words or phrases, and so on for dramatic effect. Practice reading your essay aloud beforehand so you will be comfortable with your delivery.
- Exchange essays among a small group of classmates. As a group, discuss the different subjects explained in the essays and what types of details seem most effective in explaining certain subjects. For instance, are facts important in any kind of informative essay, no matter what the subject? Are details about senses and emotions always important? As a group, draw some conclusions about the effective use of details.

*Writing & Grammar*

## NARRATIVE WRITING
# Write a Narrative Poem

A **narrative poem** is one that tells a story. As does any story, a narrative poem contains a **plot:** a series of events related to a central **conflict,** or struggle. The plot introduces the conflict, develops it, and eventually resolves it.

Like other types of poetry, narrative poems feature imaginative and musical language that is carefully chosen to communicate experiences, thoughts, and emotions. A narrative poem compresses the meaning into fewer words than a prose story would. Quite often, a narrative poem uses rhyme, meter, and imagery in telling its story.

## Learn from a Literary Model

Read the excerpt below from Ernest Lawrence Thayer's narrative poem "Casey at the Bat," on pages E157–E160 of your eBook. Note how Thayer uses imagery, meter, and rhyme in introducing the conflict, developing it, and resolving it.

### from **Casey at the Bat, by Ernest Lawrence Thayer**

The outlook wasn't brilliant for the Mudville nine that day;     *Introduces conflict*
The score stood four to two, with but one inning more to play;     *Uses meter and rhyme to help create a light tone*
And so, when Cooney died at first, and Burrows did the same,     *Adds detail to develop conflict*
A sickly silence fell upon the patrons of the game.

A straggling few got up to go in deep despair. The rest     *Conveys emotion of fans*
Clung to the hope which springs eternal in the human breast;
They thought, if only Casey could but get a whack, at that,
They'd put up even money now, with Casey at the bat.

But Flynn preceded Casey, as did also Jimmy Blake,     *Further develops conflict*
And the former was a pudding, and the latter was a fake;
So upon that stricken multitude grim melancholy sat,
For there seemed but little chance of Casey's getting to the bat.

But Flynn let drive a single, to the wonderment of all,     *Uses action to advance plot*
And Blake, the much-despised, tore the cover off the ball;
And when the dust had lifted, and they saw what had occurred,     *Uses imagery to bring game to life*
There was Jimmy safe on second, and Flynn a-hugging third.

Then from the gladdened multitude went up a joyous yell;     *Uses strong verbs*
It bounded from the mountaintop, and rattled in the dell;
It struck upon the hillside, and recoiled upon the flat;     *Suggests conflict will be resolved*
For Casey, mighty Casey, was advancing to the bat....

Oh! somewhere in this favored land the sun is shining bright;
The band is playing somewhere, and somewhere hearts are light;
And somewhere men are laughing, and somewhere children shout,
But there is no joy in Mudville—mighty Casey has struck out

Suggests happy resolution

Provides surprise unhappy resolution

1. What conflict does Thayer create in the first stanza of the poem?

   _____

   _____

2. What emotions do the fans feel, as described in the second stanza?

   _____

   _____

3. How does Thayer develop the conflict further in the third stanza?

   _____

   _____

4. What images does Thayer create in the fourth stanza? How does this use of imagery help readers envision the game?

   _____

   _____

5. In stanza 5, how does Thayer describe the fans' excitement as Casey approaches the plate?

   _____

   _____

6. In the last stanza, what does Thayer seem to suggest in the first three lines? How does the conflict seem to have been resolved? Cite details from the poem to support your answer.

   _____

   _____

7. In the last line, what do readers learn? How has the conflict actually been resolved?

   _____

   _____

8. What is the **rhyme scheme,** or pattern of rhyme in each stanza? Determine which lines rhyme.

_____

_____

## Your Assignment
### Write a Narrative Poem

To complete this assignment, follow the five stages of the writing process: Prewrite, Draft, Revise, Edit and Proofread, and Publish and Present.

## ① Prewrite

Before you write, gather your thoughts and plan your narrative poem.

### Select a Subject to Write About

In choosing a subject for your poem, consider events or experiences that involve a conflict or struggle. For example, the conflict may involve a bully picking on a timid kid (*person versus person conflict*) or a person against some act of nature, such as a flood or storm (*person versus nature conflict*). Your conflict may involve a person trying to overcome a personal fear or shortcoming, such as being afraid of heights (*person versus self conflict*) or a teenager taking a stand against on an issue such as the closing of a skateboard park (*person versus society*).

The event or experience may be one you have lived through, observed, or simply imagined. The **tone** of the poem, which is the emotional attitude it implies, may be serious or funny.

On the lines below, list four subjects you might write about, identifying the type of conflict for each one: person versus person, person versus nature, person versus self, or person versus society.

_____

_____

_____

_____

Think some more about each subject. Consider the conflict in each, including the potential for introducing, developing, and resolving the conflict in a poem. What kind of narrative, or story, can you tell to help readers understand the conflict?

Choose one subject/conflict and name it here. Also identify the type of conflict it is.

_____

_____

## State Your Purpose and Identify Your Audience

For everything you write, you should consider why you are writing it and who will be reading it. Your purpose and audience will determine what you write and how you write it.

For example, if you wanted to convince your classmates that social cliques are a serious problem in your school, you would approach the subject in a serious manner. But if you wanted to write a poem about cliques that classmates will have fun with, you will write in a silly or sarcastic manner.

One student decided to write a poem about his fear of jumping off the high-diving board at the community pool, a person versus self conflict. He decided his audience would be his fellow classmates. The student wrote this statement of purpose and audience:

> I'm going to write a narrative poem about my fear of going off the high dive so my classmates will understand why doing that is so hard for me.

Write a statement indicating your purpose and audience.

_____

_____

## Gather Your Information

Before you write, gather information about your subject. Remember that a narrative tells a story, so think about how to develop the plot, or conflict, as well as the setting, characters, background, and so on. Also think about including descriptive details, dialogue, and other elements of narration. Record your information in a chart like the one on the following page.

The student who was afraid to go off the high-diving board created the Poem Planning Chart below as he gathered information. He jotted down the setting and characters in the narrative and then worked on the plot. To plan the plot, the student broke it into three steps: introduce the conflict, develop the conflict, and resolve the conflict.

## Organize Your Information

Now that you have gathered your information, consider how best to organize it for a narrative poem. In most narratives, the actions or events are presented in the order in which they occurred, which is called **chronological order.** Details about sensory experiences, emotions, and so on are added within the framework of the action.

For instance, the student writing about jumping off the high-diving board wanted his readers to know about his feelings of envy, fear, embarrassment, and panic. He also wanted to include details about other kids' having fun, such as hearing them squeal, to show the contrast with his own feelings of panic. He fit these details in at the appropriate places within the action. This student numbered the items in his Poem Planning Chart as shown in the sample on the next page.

Number the items in your chart in the order in which you will present them.

## Poem Planning Chart

**Conflict:** Trying to overcome the fear of going off the high-diving board
**Type of conflict:** Person versus self
**Setting:** Community pool
**Character(s):** Me, friends, and other kids at pool

**Introduce the conflict:**

Feels left out ③

Sitting at side of community pool ①

Other kids diving, squealing ②

**Develop the conflict:**

Friends tease him ⑥

Wants to be like others ⑤

Wants to dive in ④

Decides to do it ⑦

Heads over to board ⑧

**Resolve the conflict:**

Climbs up ladder ⑨

Gets to top ⑩

People yelling from below—"Do it!" ⑫

Steps to edge of board ⑬

Seems really high ⑪

Raises arms—screams ⑭

Wakes up—a dream ⑮

## ② Draft

### Use the Conventions of Poetry

Whereas a work of prose, such as an essay, is written in paragraphs, a poem is written in **stanzas.** Common types of stanzas are **couplets,** which have two lines, and **quatrains,** which have four lines. The Thayer poem "Casey at the Bat" is written in quatrains.

Traditional poems, like many of those in your textbook, also have meter and rhyme. **Meter** is a regular rhythmic pattern in poetry, as shown by the number of *beats,* or stresses, in each line. Reading a poem out loud is a good way to feel the meter. **Rhyme** is the repetition of sounds at the ends of words, as with *sight* and *rite.* Many poems have **end rhyme,** in which the words rhyme at the ends of lines. A common **rhyme scheme,** or pattern of end rhymes, is to have every other line rhyme, which is an *abab* rhyme scheme. In the Thayer poem, each pair of lines rhymes, which is an *aabb* rhyme scheme.

Poetry is also different from prose in how words are used. Poets generally write with a limited number of words, and so they are particular to choose just the right words. By using literary devices such as **imagery,** in which words are used to create pictures, poets can mold language in unique ways. See the Literary Terms Handbook in your textbook for definitions and examples of other poetic devices.

## Follow the Structure of a Narrative Poem

For this assignment, write a traditional narrative poem: one that is organized into stanzas and has imagery, meter, and rhyme. Your poem should be at least three stanzas long, or about twelve lines.

Unlike an essay or report, a poem does not have an introduction, body, and conclusion. However, as a story, a narrative poem should be structured to provide an opening and a closing in addition to the details of the story. Follow this three-part structure:

1. **First stanza:** Introduce the conflict by identifying the setting, the character or characters, and the nature of the conflict.
2. **Middle stanza(s):** Develop the conflict in one or two stanzas by showing readers the anger, stress, or hurt associated with the conflict. Make it clear why the character or characters experiencing the conflict want to resolve it.
3. **Final stanza(s):** In the last one or two stanzas, resolve the conflict. In most narrative poems, the final stanza not only ends the struggle or challenge presented in the story, but it also brings about some sort of emotional comfort or relief for readers. As with the conclusion of a report or essay, the goal is to leave your readers with a specific final impression. Keep in mind, though, that you can choose to resolve your conflict with a negative outcome, as Thayer did in "Casey at the Bat."

As you draft, focus on recording the main events of the story, or narrative. At this point, don't worry about choosing the exact words and creating imagery, meter, and rhyme. You will fine-tune your language in the Revise and Edit and Proofread stages.

## ③ Revise

Be sure to allow yourself time after drafting to revise. During the Revise stage, evaluate the information you provided and the organization you followed. Have you told a good story? Will your audience be able to follow the introduction, development, and resolution of the conflict? Will they understand the emotions of the characters involved in the conflict?

Use the questions in column 1 of the Revision Checklist to identify areas that need improvement. Then, based on the evaluation, revise your draft. Use the suggestions in column 2 to fix the problems you have identified.

In revising your draft, you may decide to add, delete, or rearrange information to strengthen the argument you are making. Remember that your goal is to tell a story, most likely presenting events in the order in which they occurred. You also want readers to identify with the emotions that underlie the conflict in the story.

Read a printout of your draft, and mark your changes on the paper as you go. Think about whether your narrative poem tells a story readers will relate to and understand.

**REVISION CHECKLIST**

| Evaluate | Strengthen |
|---|---|
| ❏ Does your narrative poem have at least three stanzas, or 12 lines? | Review the discussion of stanzas, and reorganize your poem, as needed. |
| ❏ In the first stanza, does your poem introduce a conflict, as well as the setting and character(s) involved? | Add these key details to the opening stanza of the poem. |
| ❏ Does the middle stanza(s) develop the conflict, showing the emotions involved? | Add details about the events and/or emotions that will help readers feel the nature of the conflict. |
| ❏ Does the final stanza(s) resolve the conflict, finalizing the story and bringing emotional relief or comfort? | Bring the story to an end by solving the struggle or conflict and leaving readers with some final impression. |
| ❏ Does your poem have imagery, meter, and rhyme? | During the Revise and Edit and Proofread stages, continue to fine-tune the language to create imagery, meter, and rhyme. |

## ④ Edit and Proofread

After you have revised the draft of your narrative poem, edit it to check your spelling, punctuation, and grammar for errors. You may have found some of these kinds of errors already in revising your draft, but read through it again to look for them more carefully.

Also review the draft of your poem to look for ways to improve your storytelling. Will readers be able to follow the story and understand the conflict? Will they feel the emotion underlying the conflict?

Next, review your use of poetic conventions, such as meter, rhyme, and imagery. Continue to read and reread your poem, line by line and stanza by stanza, to improve the sound of the language and to add word pictures, or images. Review the Grammar & Style lesson for guidelines about using imagery.

Finally, write a title for your poem. Try to avoid creating a title that merely restates the subject of the poem in uninteresting terms. Rather, think of a title that suggests the feeling you would like readers to take away from the poem.

Retype or rewrite your narrative poem, making all of the changes you marked in editing. Then check the accuracy of this edited draft by doing a final proofread. Having a classmate read your poem is a good way to find any remaining errors.

Also reread your draft to make sure it meets the requirements of a narrative poem, as listed in the Writing Rubric below. Check off each item that applies to your essay.

Review the Original Student Draft and the Revised/Edited Student Draft to see the process one student followed in drafting and then revising and editing/proofreading his narrative poem.

## WRITING RUBRIC

A successful narrative poem has these qualities:
- ❏ Has at least three stanzas, or about 12 lines
- ❏ Introduces the conflict, setting, and character(s) in the first stanza
- ❏ Develops the conflict, including the emotions underlying it, in the middle stanza(s)
- ❏ Resolves the conflict and provides some emotional relief or comfort in the final stanza(s)
- ❏ Has both meter and rhyme
- ❏ Uses imagery to create word pictures
- ❏ Includes a title that captures the feeling of the poem
- ❏ Uses correct punctuation, grammar, spelling, and vocabulary

Did you check off each item? If not, consider making additional changes to your narrative poem.

### Original Student Draft

I sat at the side of the community pool,
feeling warm and dry and very cool.
While others squealed and dove off the high board,
I pretended to be happy while being bored.

But deep down, I felt the strange desire
to plunge into the pool, as if on fire.
And not just plunge in but to take the dive,
to feel like the others after a dive.

My friends swam over to tease me
And said, "Come on in! It's fun! You'll see."
I looked up at the board, and put on a brave front.
And with a deep breath, I was ready to stunt.

Standing at the top, it seemed much higher,
I felt like a trapeze artist on the high wire.
"Get moving!" they yelled from down below.
"You're holding us up! We want to go!"

I stepped to the edge but couldn't look down.
I wanted to do something high above the ground.
I raised my arms, gave a frightening scream,
and woke myself up. It was only a dream!

# Grammar & Style: Imagery

**Imagery** is language that creates pictures by appealing to the senses of sight, sound, touch, taste, and smell. An **image** is a picture formed in the mind of a reader.

For examples of imagery, review the fourth stanza of "Casey at the Bat," in which Ernest Lawrence Thayer creates several vivid images to help readers envision the action of a baseball game:

But Flynn **let drive a single,** to the wonderment of all,
And Blake, the much-despised, **tore the cover off the ball;**
And **when the dust had lifted,** and they saw what had occurred,
**There was Jimmy safe on second, and Flynn a-hugging third.**

The use of imagery is effective in all kinds of writing, as it adds descriptive power. In poetry, in particular, imagery helps the poet get the maximum descriptive effect with the minimum number of words. Think of how else Thayer might have written "tore the cover off the ball" had he not created this vivid image. Here's one possibility:

Blake hit the ball so hard that the seams split and the cover came off the ball.

Clearly, Thayer's poetic language is more powerful and exciting, not to mention shorter in terms of number of words. Creating images of sensory details using vivid, condensed language paints word pictures for readers.

**Exercise:** Use imagery to create word pictures for the following general descriptions.

1. Sight image: frost on a windowpane

2. Sound image: ocean waves coming to shore

3. Sight image: stars on a clear night

4. Sound image: hospital or doctor's office

Now go back to your revised poem and see if you can improve your use of imagery. Think of what images you would like readers to be able to see while they read.

## Revised/Edited Student Draft

### The High Diver

I sat at the side of the community pool,
feeling warm and dry and very cool.
While others squealed and dove off the high board,
I pretended to be happy while being **bored ignored**.

But deep down, I felt the **strange strong** desire
to plunge into the pool, as if on fire.
And not just plunge in but to take the dive,
to feel like the others, **after a dive fresh and alive**.

*Gives poem descriptive title*

*Chooses more descriptive word; improves rhyme*

*Chooses more specific adjectives*

My friends swam over to ~~tease~~ pester me
And said, "Come on in! It's fun! You'll see."
I looked up at the board, and put on a brave front.
And with a deep breath, I was ready to stunt.

**I felt I could do it, as I'd done it before,**
**Two or three times, or maybe four.**
**Up the ladder I began to climb,**
**while telling myself, "I will be just fine."**

Standing at the top, it seemed much higher,
I felt like ~~a trapeze artist on~~ the Amazing Rondini,
      atop the high wire.
"Get moving!" they yelled from down below.
"You're holding us up! We want to go!"

I stepped to the edge but couldn't look down.
I wanted to ~~do something high above the ground~~ be daring,
      ~~to act like a clown~~.
I raised my arms, gave a frightening scream,
and woke myself up. It was only a dream!

Chooses more specific verb

Conveys emotion underlying conflict

Adds stanza to further develop conflict

Puts thoughts into spoken words

Adds name to personalize

Chooses more specific words

Adds image

## ⑤ Publish and Present

- As a class, hold an "open mike" session, during which you and classmates get up and read aloud your narrative poems. Prepare for the session by practicing your oral delivery. Think about where to pause, to speak more slowly or quickly, and so on to add drama to your reading.
- Choose music to play quietly in the background while you read your poem aloud. Think about what mood you want to convey during the reading.

## DESCRIPTIVE WRITING
# Reveal Character through Dialogue

Most plays do not have a narrator, or someone to explain things to the audience. Instead, the audience must determine what is happening mostly from the **dialogue,** or the conversations between people in the play. From these conversations, the audience learns about the **characters,** or the individuals that take part in the action of a literary work: what they think and feel, what motivates them to act, what their personalities are like, and so on.

## Learn from a Literary Model

Read the excerpt below from Scene 1 of "The Dying Detective," on pages 429–447 of your textbook. This play is based on a short story by Sir Arthur Conan Doyle, who wrote the Sherlock Holmes stories, and it was dramatized by Michael and Mollie Hardwick. As you read, note how much you learn about the characters just from what they say to one another.

### from The Dying Detective, a short story by Sir Arthur Conan Doyle, Dramatized by Michael and Mollie Hardwick

**MRS. HUDSON:** He's asleep, sir.

*They approach the bed. WATSON comes round to the audience's side and looks down at HOLMES for a moment. He shakes his head gravely, then he and MRS. HUDSON move away beyond the foot of the bed. WATSON takes off his hat and coat as they talk and she takes them from him.*

> Reveals third character in scene (Sherlock Holmes)
>
> Stage directions describe setting and initial action

**WATSON:** This is dreadful, Mrs. Hudson. He was perfectly hale and hearty when I went away only three days ago.

> Establishes seriousness of situation

**MRS. HUDSON:** I know, sir. Oh, Dr. Watson, sir, I'm glad you've come back. If anyone can save Mr. Holmes, I'm sure you can.

> Reveals formal relationship between Watson and Mrs. Hudson
> Reveals Watson's occupation

**WATSON:** I shall have to know what is the matter with him first. Mrs. Hudson, please tell me, as quickly as you can, how it all came about.

**MRS. HUDSON:** Yes, sir. Mr. Holmes has been working lately on some case down near the river—Rotherhithe, I think.

**WATSON:** Yes, yes. I know.

> Suggests Watson's impatience with situation

**MRS. HUDSON:** Well, you know what he is for coming in at all hours. I was just taking my lamp to go to my bed on Wednesday night when I heard a faint knocking at the street door. I…I found Mr. Holmes there. He could hardly stand. Just muttered to me to help him up to his bed here, and he's barely spoken since.

> Shows Mrs. Hudson's familiarity with Holmes's activities and routines
> Stammering and incomplete sentences reveal Mrs. Hudson's concern

**WATSON:** Dear me!

**MRS. HUDSON:** Won't take food or drink. Just lies there, sleeping or staring in a wild sort of way.

**WATSON:** But, goodness gracious, Mrs. Hudson, why did you not send for another doctor in my absence?

*Suggests Watson's impatience*

**MRS. HUDSON:** Oh, I told him straightaway I was going to do that, sir. But he got so agitated—almost shouted that he wouldn't allow any doctor on the premises. You know how masterful he is, Dr. Watson.

*Reveals more about Mrs. Hudson's familiarity with Holmes*

**WATSON:** Indeed. But you could have telegraphed for me.

*MRS. HUDSON appears embarrassed.*

**MRS. HUDSON:** Well, sir…

**WATSON:** But you didn't. Why, Mrs. Hudson?

*Suggests more about Watson's impatience*

**MRS. HUDSON:** Sir, I don't like to tell you, but…well, Mr. Holmes said he wouldn't even have you to see him.

*Reveals more about formal relationship between Mrs. Hudson and Watson*

**WATSON:** What? This is monstrous! I, his oldest friend and…

*Reveals relationship between Watson and Holmes*

1. Describe what is happening at the start of this scene. Which characters are in the scene, and what are they doing? What is the general tone or mood of the scene?

   _____

   _____

2. What do you learn about each character from the dialogue in this scene?

   **Mrs. Hudson:** _____

   _____

   **Watson:** _____

   _____

   **Holmes:** _____

   _____

3. Based on the dialogue between Mrs. Hudson and Dr. Watson, what can you tell about their relationship? Support your answer with examples of dialogue.

   _____

   _____

4. Again, based on the dialogue, what can you tell about the relationship between Mrs. Hudson and Sherlock Holmes? Support your answer with examples.

_____

_____

5. What does the dialogue reveal about the relationship between Dr. Watson and Sherlock Holmes? Support your answer with examples of dialogue.

_____

_____

6. In some of the dialogue, the characters speak in incomplete sentences or starts and stops. For instance, when Mrs. Hudson tells Watson about what she has observed about Holmes, she stammers and says "I...I found Holmes there." How does this type of writing of dialogue affect readers?

_____

_____

## Your Assignment
### Write Dialogue That Reveals Character

To complete this assignment, follow the five stages of the writing process: Prewrite, Draft, Revise, Edit and Proofread, and Publish and Present.

# ① Prewrite

Before you write, gather your thoughts and plan your dialogue.

## Select a Subject to Write About

In choosing a subject, consider pairs of characters, such as two friends, two strangers, an alien and a human, or a parent, guardian, or teacher and a teenager. Think, too, about a situation the characters might be found in and how the characters' behavior and conversation in that situation might give insight into their personalities. Remember that you are going to write a conversation, or dialogue, between the two characters.

For instance, one student thought of a conversation she had had with her grandmother following a conflict with her mother. The student had stopped by her grandmother's house with no real purpose in mind but ended up learning from the grandmother what the mother had been like as a teen.

Identify four pairs of characters you might write about and a situation each pair might face.

_____

_____

Review each pair of characters, and think about what type of dialogue you could write for them. Think not only of the conversation that would occur in the situation you have identified but also whether you can portray that conversation realistically. The student writing about her conversation with her grandmother decided that she knew her grandmother well enough to write realistic dialogue for her.

Choose one pair of characters, and write it on the line below. Also jot down the situation the characters will be in during the dialogue.

_____

_____

## State Your Purpose and Identify Your Audience

For everything you write, you should consider why you are writing it and who will be reading it. Your purpose and audience will determine what you write and how you write it.

For example, if the student writing about talking with her grandmother intends for the dialogue to be a humorous exchange about getting along with one's parents, then she will write a conversation that is clever, funny, or perhaps sarcastic. If the same student intends to share the dialogue with parents to show them how deeply teens feel about conflict, then she will write a more serious and insightful conversation.

This student wrote the following statement of purpose and audience:

I am writing for a mixed audience of teens and parents to show that they have more in common than they might think.

Write a sentence stating your purpose and audience.

_____

_____

## Gather Your Information

Before you write, gather information about your subject. Make some notes about who the characters are and what situation they are involved in. Also decide what the outcome of the dialogue will be. Getting to this realization, decision, or action will be the goal of the conversation.

Next, make notes about what each character is like. Think carefully about what qualities you want to portray in the characters, because those qualities are what you will reveal through the dialogue. Your audience should get to know your characters based on what they say.

The student writing about her conversation with her grandmother recorded her information in the chart below. She jotted down the characters, described the situation they were in, and determined the outcome they would reach. Then the student made some notes about how to portray the characters. She decided that she wanted to portray the grandmother as concerned, patient, and wise. These qualities could be revealed in the grandmother's being understanding and reflective and giving good advice. The student decided that she wanted to portray the teen as bright and independent. These qualities could be revealed in the teen's being impatient and feeling misunderstood.

Finally, the student thought about things each character might actually say. She recorded these pieces of conversation in the chart below.

**Dialogue Planning Chart**
**Characters:** Teen and grandmother
**Situation:** Teen has conflict with mother; goes to see grandmother
**Outcome:** Teen understands problems mother had at her age

| | Grandmother | Teen |
|---|---|---|
| **Qualities of Character** | Concerned, patient, wise | Bright, independent |
| **Things Character Would Say** | I'm happy you stopped by. ① | I have a lot going on. ② |
| | Tell me what happened. ③ | You won't understand. ⑦ |
| | I remember when your mother was a teenager. ⑧ | My mom isn't fair. ⑥ |
| | Did you have a fight with your mother? ⑤ | I'm not a child. ④ |
| | We had our share of problems. ⑩ | She hates all my friends. ⑦ |
| | Some lessons are learned the hard way. ⑳ | My mom never did anything wrong. ⑨ |
| | Didn't like her friends. ⑫ | What did she do wrong? ⑪ |
| | We took away some privileges. ⑭ | Did you ground her? ⑬ |
| | Trouble with friends— lied about her. ⑰ | What did she do? ⑭, ⑯ |
| | No—not sure what happened. ⑲ | Did they stay friends? ⑱ |

## Organize Your Information

Now that you have gathered your information, consider how best to organize it for the dialogue. Logically, the first statement or two of the conversation should establish the situation—for instance, where the conversation is taking place and what circumstances have brought these characters together. Also logically, the final statement or two should bring the conversation to a close after achieving the outcome.

With these opening and closing goals in mind, organize the rest of the dialogue like the back-and-forth exchange of a typical conversation. Number the statements of the things the characters would say in the order in which you will present them. See the numbering in the Dialogue Planning Chart for an example.

## ② Draft

For this assignment, plan on writing at least 15 lines of dialogue. One line of dialogue can include as little as a single word or as much as several sentences. Review the Literary Model at the start of this lesson to see how different lines of dialogue can be in terms of length and detail.

### Formatting Your Dialogue

For this assignment, follow the format of dialogue in the script of a play, as shown in the Literary Model. Here are some basic guidelines:

1. To indicate which character is speaking, type or write the character's name in boldface or all capital letters. Add a colon after the name.
2. Type or write what the characters say in regular (roman) print. Do not put quotation marks around what the characters say.
3. Allow extra space between separate lines of dialogue, or where you switch from one character to another.

### Writing Realistic Dialogue

Keep in mind that you want the characters to sound like real people. That means that what they say, believe, and think about should be appropriate for how old they are, what level of education they have, what experiences they have had, what situation they are in, and so on. The grandmother in the student example, for instance, should say things that reflect the life experiences of someone, say, in her seventies.

You also want your characters to sound like different people. The grandmother and the teen, for instance, should not speak in the same way. Think about what types of language and patterns of speech you can use to make your characters sound different. Develop an authentic, consistent voice for each character.

Finally, keep in mind that in most conversations, people use fairly informal language. That is, they speak in short sentences and even sentence fragments, and they use contractions and popular expressions. Tailor the formality of the language to the qualities of each character.

## ③ Revise

Be sure to allow yourself time after drafting to revise. During the Revise stage, evaluate the information you provided and the organization you followed. Does your dialogue sound like a real conversation? Does what each character says reveal what he or she is like?

Use the questions in column 1 of the Revision Checklist to identify areas that need improvement. Then, based on the evaluation, revise your draft. Use the suggestions in column 2 to fix the problems you have identified.

In revising your draft, you may decide to add, delete, or rearrange information to strengthen the dialogue. Remember that your goal is to reveal the qualities of your characters through what they say. Making the conversation as realistic as possible will help you achieve this.

Read a printout of your draft, and mark your changes on the paper as you go. Think about whether your dialogue unfolds like an actual conversation between two real people.

## REVISION CHECKLIST

| Evaluate | Strengthen |
|---|---|
| ❑ Is your dialogue formatted correctly, like the script of a play? | Review the formatting guidelines given, and see the Literary Model for an example. |
| ❑ Do the first several lines of dialogue indicate the situation the characters are involved in or why they are talking? | Establish or clarify the situation so readers will know where, when, or why the conversation is taking place. |
| ❑ Does the dialogue reveal the qualities of each character? | Add details that bring out the qualities you identified for each character in your planning chart. |
| ❑ Does the dialogue sound realistic? | Develop an authentic, consistent voice for each character that reflects his or her age, education, experiences, and so on. |
| ❑ Does the dialogue end by reaching the desired outcome? | Review the outcome you stated in your planning chart, and redirect the dialogue to achieve that goal. |

## ④ Edit and Proofread

After you have revised your draft, edit it to check your spelling, punctuation, and grammar for errors. You may have found some of these kinds of errors already in the Revise stage, but read through your draft again to look for errors more carefully.

Also review your draft to look for ways to improve the portrayal of the characters in your dialogue. Focus on writing realistic dialogue that makes your characters sound like real people. Work on developing an authentic, consistent voice for each character. Review the Grammar & Style lesson for guidelines about using contractions.

Retype or rewrite your dialogue, making all of the changes you marked in editing. Then check the accuracy of this edited draft by doing a final proofread. Reading your work aloud is a good way to find any remaining errors.

Also reread your draft to make sure it meets the requirements of dialogue revealing character, as listed in the Writing Rubric on page 66. Check off each item that applies to your work.

Review the Original Student Draft and the Revised/Edited Student Draft to see the process one student followed in drafting and then revising and editing/proofreading her dialogue.

A successful dialogue revealing character has these qualities:
- ❏ Is formatted correctly, like the script of a play
- ❏ Indicates in the first few lines the situation the characters are involved in or why they are talking
- ❏ Reveals the qualities of each character through what is said
- ❏ Sounds realistic, reflecting an authentic, consistent voice for each character
- ❏ Ends by reaching the desired outcome
- ❏ Uses contractions accurately and appropriately
- ❏ Uses correct punctuation, grammar, spelling, and vocabulary

Did you check off each item? If not, consider making additional changes to your dialogue.

## Original Student Draft

**Grandmother:** I'm so happy you stopped by! I don't see enough of you these days.

**Teenager:** I know, Grandma. I have a lot going on.

**Grandmother:** Well, you seem like you have something on your mind. So, child, tell me what happened.

**Teenager:** I'm not a child, Grandma! Although that's the way Mom treats me!

**Grandmother:** So, is that what this is about? Did you have a fight with your mother?

**Teenager:** My mom is not fair! She hates all my friends! But you won't understand.

**Grandmother:** I remember when your mother was a teenager. I might be able to help.

**Teenager:** My mom never did anything wrong, did she?

**Grandmother:** We had our share of problems.

**Teenager:** What kinds of problems could you have had with my mom?

**Grandmother:** It was mostly about her friends. She knew some bad kids. They seemed to be in trouble all the time. We were afraid your mother would end up in trouble, too.

**Teenager:** Really? Did you ground her?

**Grandmother:** In those days, we did not call it that. But she did lose some of her privileges. There were some weekends she had to stay home—no friends!

**Teenager:** Oh, really? What did she do about that?

**Grandmother:** She was not happy! But then one of those weekends, her friends got in trouble with the police and tried to say she was involved, too. We could prove she was home, so nothing happened. But your mom was really hurt that her friends had lied about her.

# Grammar & Style: Contractions

As noted earlier, most people's conversation is fairly informal and includes the use of contractions. A **contraction** is formed by combining a pronoun and a verb or the words in a verb phrase. One or more letters are dropped and replaced with an apostrophe.

Commonly used contractions formed from the pronouns *I, you,* and *we* include the following:

I'm (I am)            I've (I have)         I'll (I will)
you're (you are)      you've (you have)     you'll (you will)
we're (we are)        we've (we have)       we'll (we will)

Commonly used contractions formed from verb phrases with *not* include these:

isn't (is not)        wasn't (was not)      doesn't (does not)
won't (will not)      can't (can not)       don't (do not)

Using contractions like these in writing dialogue will add to the realism of the conversation. After all, most people say *isn't* instead of *is not* and *I'm* instead of *I am* in everyday speech.

Some contractions are often used incorrectly, however, because they sound like other words. Be careful in using the contractions *you're, who's,* and *it's* in place of *your, whose,* and *its.* Look at these examples:

**Incorrect:** *You're* picture looks nice in the office.
**Correct:** *Your* picture looks nice in the office.

**Incorrect:** *Who's* tennis racket is this?
**Correct:** *Whose* tennis racket is this?

**Incorrect:** *Its* mine.
**Correct:** *It's* mine.

**Exercise:** Revise each of the following sentences to use a contraction in place of two words or to replace an incorrectly used contraction with the correct word.

1. Its our responsibility to correct the problem.

2. We will not be able to go on vacation this year.

3. All you can do is try you're best.

4. Whatever you decide, I will be glad to help.

5. It does not look good for our team.

Now go back to your draft and see if you used contractions appropriately and correctly. Make any necessary corrections.

**Teenager:** Did she stay friends with them?

**Grandmother:** No, she did not. I am not sure whether she dropped them or they dropped her. She never really said. But she felt sad for a long time. Some lessons are learned the hard way.

## Revised/Edited Draft

**Grandmother:** I'm so happy you stopped by! I don't see enough of you these days.

**Teenager:** I know, Grandma. I have a lot going on.

**Grandmother:** Well, you seem like you have something on your mind. So, child, tell me what happened.

**Teenager:** I'm not a child, Grandma! Although that's the way Mom treats me!

> Establishes situation
> Suggests nature of relationship between characters
> Reveals Teenager's lifestyle
> Reveals Grandmother's personality
> Reveals Teenager's feelings and personality

**Grandmother:** So, is that what this is about? ~~Did you have~~ **You had** a fight with your mother?

**Teenager:** My mom ~~is not~~ **isn't** fair! She hates all my friends! But you won't understand.

**Grandmother:** I remember when your mother was a teenager. I might be able to help.

**Teenager: Seriously, Grandma!** My mom never did anything wrong, did she?

**Grandmother: Don't be so sure!** We had our share of problems.

**Teenager:** What kinds of problems could you have had with my mom? **Did she not fold her napkin properly? Or forget to make her bed?**

**Grandmother: As I recall**, It was mostly about her friends. She knew some ~~bad kids~~ **real troublemakers.** They ~~seemed to be~~ **were just** in trouble all the time. We were afraid your mother would end up in trouble, too.

**Teenager:** Really? Did you ground her?

**Grandmother:** In those days, we ~~did not~~ **didn't** call it that. But she did lose some of her privileges. There were some weekends she had to stay home—no friends!

**Teenager:** Oh, really? What did she do about that?

> Makes dialogue more informal
>
> Uses contraction for consistency in Teenager's voice
>
> Adds expressions for authenticity
>
> Adds comment to reveal personality
>
> Adds expressions for authenticity
>
> Shows Teenager's curiosity
> Adds contraction
>
> Shows Teenager's curiosity

**Grandmother:** She ~~was not~~ **wasn't** happy, **believe me!** But then one of those weekends, her friends got in trouble with the police and tried to say she was involved, too. We could prove she was home, so **~~nothing happened~~ that put an end to that.** But your mom was really hurt that her friends had lied about her.

Adds contraction

Adds expressions for authenticity

**Teenager:** Did she stay friends with them?

**Grandmother:** No, she ~~did not~~ **didn't.** ~~I am~~ **I'm** not sure whether she dropped them or they dropped her. She never really said. But she felt sad for a long time. Some lessons are learned the hard way.

Adds contractions

Arrives at outcome

## ⑤ Publish and Present

- Exchange papers with a classmate, and practice reading each dialogue aloud. Add dramatic effects, such as changing the quality of your voice, as if you are performing in a play. Perform your dramatizations for the entire class. Ask audience members to jot down two or three qualities of each character in each dialogue. Then discuss how successful each dialogue portrayed its characters through conversation.
- With several classmates, select another excerpt from "The Dying Detective," on pages 430–447 of your textbook. Together, plan how to dramatize that part of the play, and then deliver your performance to the class. Again, ask for audience feedback.

Name: _____   Date: _____

NARRATIVE WRITING
# Write a Tall Tale

The **tall tale** is a story, often lighthearted or humorous, that contains highly exaggerated, unrealistic elements. The exaggerations generally involve impossible or unrealistic events, often including a character with extraordinary qualities.

As a form of folk literature, a tall tale reflects the culture from which it comes. In fact, many tall tales are about the adventures of American folk heroes on the frontier, including Paul Bunyan, Calamity Jane, Pecos Bill, Davie Crockett, Annie Oakley, and Johnny Appleseed. Some tall tales explain how certain mountains, lakes, and other geographic features came to exist.

## Learn from a Literary Model

Read the following excerpts from "Pecos Bill," a tall tale by Adrien Stoutenburg, on pages 556–566 of your textbook. Note the exaggerated characters and events and the lighthearted tone in this story about a mythical American cowboy. Note, too, that this Literary Model includes two scenes from different parts of the story. For the complete story, see your textbook.

### from **Pecos Bill, by Adrien Stoutenburg**

[Pecos Bill] straddled a mountain lion he had tamed and rode with the cowboy toward the cowboy's ranch. On the way to the ranch, a big rattlesnake reared up in front of them. The cowboy galloped off, but Bill jumped from his mount and faced the snake.

> Suggests unrealistic act

> Character shown to be brave

"I'll let you have the first three bites, Mister Rattler, just to be fair. Then I'm going to beat the poison out of you until you behave yourself!"

> Uses dialogue to advance action

That is just what Bill did. He whipped the snake around until it stretched out like a thirty-foot rope. Bill looped the rattler-rope in one hand, got back on his lion, and caught up with the cowboy. To entertain himself, he made a loop out of the snake and tossed it over the head of an armadillo plodding along through the cactus. Next he lassoed several Gila monsters.

> Boasting adds to characterization

> Use of action verbs creates imagery

One of the most exciting things Bill did was to find himself the wildest, strongest, most beautiful horse that ever kicked up the Texas dust. He was a mighty, golden mustang, and even Bill couldn't outrun that horse. To catch the mustang, Bill had the cowboys rig up a huge slingshot and shoot him high over the cactus and greasewood. When Bill landed in front of the mustang, the horse was so surprised he stopped short, thrusting out his front legs stiff as rifle barrels. The mustang had been going so fast that his hoofs drove into the ground, and he was stuck. Bill leaped on the animal's back, yanked on his golden mane, and pulled him free. The mustang was

> Uses matter-of-fact tone to add to humor

> Exaggerates qualities of other characters

> Enhances tone using folksy similes: *as stiff as rifle barrels* and *as gentle as a soft wind in a thatch of Jimson weed*

so thankful for being pulled from the trap that he swung his head around
and gave Pecos Bill a smacking kiss. From then on, the horse was as
gentle as a soft wind in a thatch of Jimson weed.

1. In the first paragraph, what exaggerated action has Pecos Bill already
   performed?

   _____

   _____

2. In paragraph 2, what does the use of dialogue add to the tale?

   _____

   _____

3. In paragraph 3, what does the use of action verbs add to the tale? Support your
   answer with specific examples.

   _____

   _____

4. What exaggerated actions are performed by characters other than Pecos Bill?

   _____

   _____

5. How does the author create a lighthearted, folksy tone through his storytelling?

   _____

   _____

   _____

## Your Assignment
### Write a Tall Tale

To complete this assignment, follow the five stages of the writing process: Prewrite,
Draft, Revise, Edit and Proofread, and Publish and Present.

# ① Prewrite

Before you write, gather your thoughts and plan your tall tale.

## Select a Subject to Write About

In planning your tall tale, consider what types of qualities you want your main
character to have. For instance, what remarkable physical features or abilities should
he or she possess? Also consider in what settings or situations these features and
abilities would be useful. For instance, Pecos Bill was the ultimate cowboy of the
American West, so he had extraordinary abilities at riding, roping, and so on. These
abilities would not be useful for a character in a modern setting, however.

List four characters you might write a tall tale about.

_____

_____

_____

_____

To select one character, think more closely about the features and abilities each character would have and in what setting or situation he or she would exist. About which character could you tell the most clever story?

One student decided to write a tall tale about a skateboarding baby. The baby would be born with amazing skateboarding knowledge and ability, as if he were an experienced skateboarder. The situation would involve the baby performing amazing feats and drawing a crowd.

Choose one character, and write his or her name or description on the line below. Also jot down two or three qualities this character will have and the setting or situation in which he or she will exist.

_____

_____

## State Your Purpose and Identify Your Audience

For everything you write, you should consider why you are writing it and who will be reading it. Your purpose and audience will determine what you write and how you write it.

In writing a tall tale, your main purpose is to entertain your audience. Determining the nature of that audience, however, is critical. You have to be sure your audience will understand the character and the actions he or she performs. Your story will be lost on an audience that cannot relate to the character and what he or she does.

For example, the student writing about the skateboarding baby realized that anyone who was not familiar with skateboarding, including many adults, would not likely be able to relate to his story. An audience of teens, however, would be more likely to understand and enjoy the tale. This student wrote the following statement of purpose and audience:

I am writing a tall tale about a baby skateboarder to entertain an audience of teens who know about skateboarding.

Write a sentence stating your purpose and audience.

_____

_____

*Writing & Grammar*     © Carnegie Learning, Inc.

## Gather Your Information

Before you write, gather information about your subject. Start with the notes you have already made about the qualities and abilities of your character and the setting or situation he or she is in. Then fill in specific details about action and dialogue to develop the story. Record your information in a chart like the one below.

For the tall tale about the skateboarding baby, the student started by jotting down the character and the setting/situation. Then the student brainstormed a list of actions the character would perform during the story.

### Tall Tale Planning Chart

| Character | Baby skateboarder (A. J.) |
|---|---|
| Setting/Situation | Baby performs amazing acts and draws attention |
| Actions | Baby picks up board, spins wheels, examines things ① |
| | Baby gets on board, knows what to do ② |
| | Performs tricks ④ |
| | Goes outside—jumps sidewalk ③ |
| | Ends up on TV news ⑥ |
| | Draws crowd ⑤ |

## Organize Your Information

Now that you have gathered your information, consider how best to organize it for your tall tale. Remember that narratives usually follow **chronological order,** such that events are presented in the order in which they occur. This type of organization makes sense for most kinds of stories, including tall tales.

Number the actions you have brainstormed in the order in which you will present them. Use the sample student chart as a model.

## ② Draft

Before you begin drafting your tall tale, decide who will narrate your story. Will you use a **first-person point of view,** in which the narrator participates in the story, or a **third-person point of view,** in which the narrator observes the story?

In drafting, think about other stories you have read. For instance, most stories begin by identifying the **setting** and the **characters.** Then the action, or **plot,** of the story begins. Some sort of **conflict** is introduced and eventually solved, bringing the story to a **resolution,** or close.

Follow this basic pattern in writing your tall tale. In the first paragraph or two, introduce the main character and place him or her in a specific setting—one in which his or her unique features or abilities can be used. If the narrator is a character in the story, introduce him or her, as well.

In the following paragraphs, present the main character in action. Your plot can include one main event that you describe in detail or a series of smaller events that lead up to a larger event. The conflict may involve pitting your character against another character, a force of nature, or some other obstacle.

The ending of your tall tale should resolve the conflict and leave readers with a final impression of how amazing your character is.

As you write, remember that your purpose is to entertain your readers by telling an outlandish tale. Don't be afraid to exaggerate. The more bizarre the character and his or her actions, the better the story and the more humorous the outcome.

# ③ Revise

Be sure to allow yourself time after drafting to revise. During the Revise stage, evaluate the information you provided and the organization you followed. Have you told an outlandish tale? Will your audience be entertained?

Use the questions in column 1 of the Revision Checklist to identify areas that need improvement. Then, based on the evaluation, revise your draft. Use the suggestions in column 2 to fix the problems you have identified.

In revising your draft, you may decide to add, delete, or rearrange information to strengthen the story you are telling. Remember that your goal is to entertain your readers with a bizarre story. Presenting information in chronological order is effective for most kinds of narratives.

Read a printout of your draft, and mark your changes on the paper as you go. Think about whether your story presents an unusual character and develops an amusing tale.

 REVISION CHECKLIST

| Evaluate | Strengthen |
| --- | --- |
| ❏ Is your tall tale told from a specific point of view? | Determine whether the narrator of your story will be a participant (first person) or observer (third person). |
| ❏ Does your tall tale establish the setting and introduce the character or characters in the first paragraph or two? | Provide readers with needed details about when and where the story is taking place and who it's about. |
| ❏ Does the plot develop a conflict? | Trace the plot and ensure that it develops a conflict through a series of small events or by building to one large event. |
| ❏ Does the plot include exaggerated actions that demonstrate the unusual abilities and qualities of the main character? | Add details and exaggerate the actions to show how unique the character is. |
| ❏ Does the tale end by resolving the conflict and leaving the reader with a final impression of the character? | End the story with an event that shows the character's unique abilities and qualities. |

*Writing & Grammar*

# ④ Edit and Proofread

After you have revised your draft, edit it to check your spelling, punctuation, and grammar for errors. You may have found some of these kinds of errors already in revising your draft, but read through it again to look for them more carefully.

Also review your draft to look for ways to improve the narrative quality of your writing. Think of how you can tell an outlandish story that will entertain your readers. Review the Grammar & Style lesson for guidelines about developing the appropriate tone.

Retype or rewrite your tall tale, making all of the changes you marked in editing. Then check the accuracy of this edited draft by doing a final proofread. Having a classmate read your story is a good way to find any remaining errors.

Also reread your draft to make sure it meets the requirements of a tall tale, as listed in the Writing Rubric below. Check off each item that applies to your story.

Review the Original Student Draft and the Revised/Edited Student Draft to see the process one student followed in drafting and then revising and editing/proofreading his tall tale.

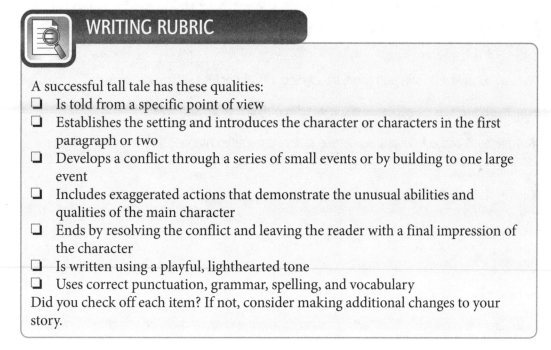

**WRITING RUBRIC**

A successful tall tale has these qualities:
- ❏ Is told from a specific point of view
- ❏ Establishes the setting and introduces the character or characters in the first paragraph or two
- ❏ Develops a conflict through a series of small events or by building to one large event
- ❏ Includes exaggerated actions that demonstrate the unusual abilities and qualities of the main character
- ❏ Ends by resolving the conflict and leaving the reader with a final impression of the character
- ❏ Is written using a playful, lighthearted tone
- ❏ Uses correct punctuation, grammar, spelling, and vocabulary

Did you check off each item? If not, consider making additional changes to your story.

# Grammar & Style: Tone

**Tone** is the emotional attitude toward the reader or subject implied by a literary work. The tone can be serious or sarcastic, funny or sad, angry or friendly.

In a tall tale, the tone should be playful and lighthearted. The main way a writer creates this tone is by treating exaggerated, unrealistic people and events in a matter-of-fact way, as if they are commonplace. Another way of creating a playful tone is by choosing active verbs that create images in readers' minds.

Review these examples from "Pecos Bill," the Literary Model at the beginning of the lesson. Note the matter-of-fact treatment of the subjects and the use of active verbs:

[Pecos Bill] straddled a mountain lion he had tamed and rode with the cowboy toward the cowboy's ranch.

He whipped the snake around until it stretched out like a thirty-foot rope.

The mustang was so thankful for being pulled from the trap that he swung his head around and gave Pecos Bill a smacking kiss.

A final way of creating a light, playful tone is by using similes. Recall that a **simile** is a comparison of two seemingly unlike things using the connective word *like* or *as*. The similes in "Pecos Bill" add to the folksy Western feel of the story:

The horse was so surprised he stopped short, thrusting out his front legs *stiff as rifle barrels.*

From then on, the horse was *as gentle as a soft wind in a thatch of Jimson weed.*

**Exercise:** Rewrite each of the following sentences in an exaggerated manner but with a lighthearted, playful tone.

1. My brother eats a lot for breakfast.

2. The weather today is very cold.

3. My dog has very good hearing.

4. I don't like broccoli.

Now go back to your tall tale and look at each sentence. Make the changes needed to achieve a more playful tone.

## Original Student Draft

When my brother A. J. was born, everything about him seemed normal. Then one day, when he was about ten months old, that all changed.

I was babysitting A. J., and we were sitting on the front stoop. To entertain him, I started spinning the wheels on my skateboard. Then A. J. reached over and, with his little hand, began spinning the wheels himself.

Next, A. J. picked up the board! I wondered how this baby could possibly have the strength to do that! He turned the board over and examined it.

Then A. J. got on the board. He couldn't even walk yet, but there he was, standing on my skateboard. He saw the ramp I had made on the stoop, and he crawled over to it, dragging the board. Before I could grab him, A. J. had gone down the ramp, kickturned, and ridden back up. Then he did it again!

I brought A. J. over to the sidewalk. About fifteen yards away, an orange cone had been placed by the sidewalk to keep people from stepping on the wet cement. A. J. seemed to know exactly what to do. He and the skateboard took off toward the cone and nollied over it. This was a trick many of my friends couldn't do!

Before I knew it, a crowd had gathered in front of our house to watch A. J. perform. People were clapping and throwing coins toward my baby brother. "Do another one!" they yelled. So A. J. did 50-50, grinding with both trucks. Then the television news cameras came to film A. J. for the six o'clock news.

## Revised/Edited Student Draft

When my brother A. J. was born, everything about him seemed normal. Then one day, when he was about ten months old, that all changed.

I was babysitting A. J., and we were sitting on the front stoop. To entertain him, I started spinning the wheels on my skateboard. Then A. J. reached over and, with his little hand, began spinning the wheels himself. **They were going faster than I had ever spun them, whistling and throwing off heat.**

Next, A. J. picked up the board! I ~~wondered~~ **asked myself, "How could how** this baby ~~could~~ possibly have the strength to do that~~!~~**?"** He turned the board over and examined it**, as if he were some kind of engineer or scientist**.

Then A. J. got on the board. He couldn't even walk yet, but there he was, standing on my skateboard. **"How could this be?" I wondered.** He saw the ramp I had made on the stoop, and he crawled over to it, dragging the board **behind his tiny little body.** Before I could grab him, A. J. had gone down the ramp, kickturned, and ridden back up. Then he did it again!

Introduces characters

Establishes setting/ situation

Adds detail for exaggeration

Creates dialogue to comment on situation

Adds simile to create light tone

Creates more dialogue

Creates image

I brought A. J. over to the sidewalk. About fifteen yards away, an orange cone had been placed by the sidewalk to keep people from stepping on the wet cement. A. J. seemed to know exactly what to do**, like he had been skateboarding for years and years.** He and the skateboard took off toward the cone and nollied over it. This was a trick many of my friends couldn't do! **Here was this baby in diapers doing it with ease!**

Before I knew it, a **huge** crowd had gathered in front of our house to watch A. J. perform. People were clapping and throwing coins toward my baby brother. "Do another one!" they yelled. So A. J. did 50-50, grinding with both trucks. ~~Then~~ **The next thing I knew,** the television news cameras came to film A. J. for the six o'clock news.

**While everyone watched in awe, A. J. used a parked car as a jump and flew off the end, sailing over the crowd. Only he didn't come down! He and my skateboard aired over the crowd, the TV trucks, and then the three-story house across the street.**

**After some searching, I found my baby brother two blocks away, sitting on my skateboard and crying "Mama."**

Margin notes (right column):

- Adds detail for exaggeration
- Adds comment
- Adds detail for exaggeration
- Creates light storytelling tone
- Adds action to bring plot to climax and then resolution
- Leaves readers with final impression of character

## ⑤ Publish and Present

- Hold a Tall Tale Competition among your classmates. Start by exchanging stories with three or four classmates. As a group, decide on the most outlandish and entertaining story. Then have the author of the story read it aloud to the class. The selected authors from the other small groups should do the same. After the entire class has heard all the stories, take a class vote and select the best tall tale.
- Do some research about a character from a tall tale about the American West, such as Paul Bunyan, Calamity Jane, Pecos Bill, Davie Crockett, or Annie Oakley. Determine whether this character was a real person, a completely fictitious character, or something in between (that is, based on or similar to a real person). Find evidence to support your opinion. Present your findings in a one-page report.

# PART II

# GRAMMAR & STYLE

**LESSON 1**

# The Sentence and Parts of Speech

## The Sentence and Its Functions

From the time you entered school, you probably have been speaking and writing in sentences. In the English language, the sentence is the basic unit of meaning.

A sentence is a group of words that expresses a complete thought. Every sentence has two basic parts: a subject and a predicate. The subject tells whom or what the sentence is about. The predicate tells information about the subject—what the subject is, what the subject does, or what happens to the subject.

EXAMPLE

**sentence**    The young pianist | studied the difficult sonata.
         **(subject)**          **(predicate)**

A group of words that does not have both a subject and a predicate is called a **sentence fragment**. A sentence fragment does not express a complete thought.

EXAMPLES

| | |
|---|---|
| **sentence fragment** | The cabinetmaker. (The fragment does not have a predicate. The group of words does not answer the question *What did the cabinetmaker do?*) |
| **sentence fragment** | Sharpened the carving tools. (The fragment does not have a subject. The group of words does not answer the question *Who sharpened the carving tools?*) |
| **sentence fragment** | At his bench. (The fragment does not have a subject or predicate. The group of words does not tell what the sentence is about or tell what the subject does.) |
| **complete sentence** | The cabinetmaker sharpened the carving tools at his bench. |

## EXERCISE 1

### Identifying Sentences and Sentence Fragments

Identify each of the following groups of words as either a complete sentence or a sentence fragment. Write *S* for sentence or *F* for fragment.

_____ 1. Waiting for the yeast bread to rise and bake.

_____ 2. Charles White was a pioneer of American mural art.

_____ 3. The artisan cut the red and blue glass for the window.

_____ 4. Deep inside the hot pottery kiln.

_____ 5. Her palette glistened with globs of fresh paint.

_____ 6. In the cabinetmaker's shop behind the bench.

_____ 7. A friend as well as a talented chef.　　　　_____ 8. Into the basket he gathered the garden's harvest.

## EXERCISE 2

### Understanding Sentences and Their Basic Parts

Some of the following groups of words are missing a subject or predicate or both. Tell what part is missing, then revise the sentence to include the missing part. If the group of words contains both a subject and a predicate, write *sentence*.

> EXAMPLE
> The graceful ballet dancer.
> (predicate missing, The graceful ballet dancer *pirouetted across the stage.*)

1. In the artist's studio.

_____

2. The model patiently posed for the artist.

_____

3. Applies make-up and costume.

_____

4. A modern painting.

_____

5. On the brightly lit stage.

_____

6. The photographic image slowly emerged.

_____

7. Untidy piles of paint tubes.

_____

8. Wrote about her childhood experiences.

_____

## EXERCISE 3

### Using Complete Sentences in Your Writing

Write a paragraph describing a skill or talent that someone has and that you admire. Perhaps he or she is an artist, a chef, a musician, or a woodworker. Why do you admire his or her skill? What does he or she make or do with the skill? Make sure that each sentence in your paragraph contains a subject and predicate. Use your own sheet of paper for this exercise.

# Functions of Sentences

There are four different kinds of sentences: *declarative, interrogative, imperative,* and *exclamatory*. Each kind of sentence has a different purpose. You can vary the tone and mood of your writing by using the four different sentence types. Read the example sentences aloud and notice how your voice changes to express each sentence's different meaning.

- A **declarative sentence** makes a statement. It ends with a period.

  EXAMPLE
  Aaron wants to visit his cousins in Chicago.

- An **interrogative sentence** asks a question. It ends with a question mark.

  EXAMPLE
  Will Aaron visit his cousins in Chicago?

- An **imperative sentence** gives an order or makes a request. It ends with a period or an exclamation point. An imperative sentence has an understood subject. The understood subject is often *you*.

  EXAMPLE
  (You) Please travel safely.
  (You) Read some more of his books.

- An **exclamatory sentence** expresses strong feeling. It ends with an exclamation point.

  EXAMPLE
  Aaron can't wait to leave on his trip!

## EXERCISE 4

### Identifying Different Kinds of Sentences in Literature

Identify each of the eight sentences in the passage as *declarative, interrogative, imperative,* or *exclamatory*. Write your answers on the corresponding lines below.

¹"I'm not looking for your treasure," Greg answered, smiling. "If you have one."
"What you mean, *if* I have one," Lemon Brown said. ²"Every man got a treasure. ³You don't know that, you must be a fool!"
⁴"Sure," Greg said as he sat on the sofa and put one leg over the back.
⁵"What do you have, gold coins?"
⁶"Don't worry none about what I got," Lemon Brown said. ⁷"You know who I am?"
⁸"You told me your name was orange or lemon or something like that."

*from "The Treasure of Lemon Brown," page 16*
*Walter Dean Myers*

1. _____   4. _____

2. _____   5. _____

3. _____   6. _____

4. _____   8. _____

# EXERCISE 5

## Understanding the Functions of Sentences

Identify the following sentences as *declarative*, *imperative*, *interrogative*, or *exclamatory*. Then revise each sentence according to the directions in parentheses.

EXAMPLE
Did you see the horse in the pasture? (Change into an imperative sentence.)
(interrogative; imperative: *See the horse in the pasture.*)

1. Tell me where you want to travel. (Change into an interrogative sentence.)

   _____

2. Will you please answer the phone? (Change into an imperative sentence.)

   _____

3. I'm hungry for a mushroom and cheese pizza. (Change into an interrogative sentence.)

   _____

4. Is the mirror cracked? (Change into an exclamatory sentence.)

   _____

5. Who is knocking on the door? (Change into a declarative sentence.)

   _____

6. Spring is my favorite season! (Change into a declarative sentence.)

   _____

7. Did you know that Frank tells very funny stories? (Change into an exclamatory sentence.)

   _____

# EXERCISE 6

## Using Different Kinds of Sentences in Your Writing

On your own paper, write a script for a radio commercial advertising a product that you use every day. Your commercial may be serious, humorous, or persuasive in tone. Use all four kinds of sentences in your script. Then take turns with your classmates reading your scripts aloud. Consider how using the four kinds of sentences makes your scripts more expressive.

*Writing & Grammar*

**LESSON 2**

# Subjects and Predicates: The Basic Building Blocks in a Sentence

Just as the sentence is the basic building block of the English language, the subject and predicate are the basic building blocks in a sentence. Every sentence has two basic parts: a subject and a predicate. The **subject** tells whom or what the sentence is about. The **predicate** tells information about the subject—what the subject is, what the subject does, or what happens to the subject.

EXAMPLE

|  | (subject) | (predicate) |
|---|---|---|
| **sentence** | The brilliant scientist \| | examined the difficult theorem. |

To find the subject, ask who or what performs the action of the verb.

EXAMPLE
Who examined the difficult theorem? (*the brilliant scientist,* subject)
What did the brilliant scientist do? (*examined the difficult theorem,* predicate)

## EXERCISE 1

### Identifying Subjects and Predicates in Literature

Draw a vertical line between the subject and predicate in each sentence.

I was there in the autumn. I wanted quiet, isolation, to do some troublesome

writing. I wanted mountain air to blow out the malaria from too long a time in the

subtropics. I was homesick, too, for the flaming of maples in October, and for corn

shocks and pumpkins and black-walnut trees and the lift of hills. I found them all,

living in a cabin that belonged to the orphanage, half a mile beyond the orphanage

farm. When I took the cabin, I asked for a boy or man to come and chop wood for

the fireplace. The first few days were warm, I found what wood I needed about the

cabin, no one came, and I forgot the order.

*from "A Mother in Mannville," page 29*
*Marjorie Kinnan Rawlings*

# EXERCISE 2

## Understanding Subjects and Predicates

Items 1–5 include a list of subjects; items 6–10 include a list of predicates. Write a sentence for each subject or predicate listed, adding the missing part and any other details to create a clear, complete sentence.

1. The black and white photographs

   _____

   _____

2. Today's teenagers

   _____

   _____

3. A group of explorers

   _____

   _____

4. The full, bright moon

   _____

   _____

5. The endurance test

   _____

   _____

6. sat on the riverbank

   _____

   _____

7. are hoping for an early spring

   _____

   _____

8. demands fair and equal treatment

   _____

   _____

9. provided shelter from the sun

_____

_____

10. adopted the crying kittens

_____

_____

## EXERCISE 3

### Using Subjects and Predicates in Your Writing

Write a paragraph that closely describes an immediate scene, such as the view outside a window. Make sure each sentence includes a subject and predicate and creates a clear picture.

_____

_____

_____

_____

_____

_____

_____

_____

_____

_____

_____

_____

**LESSON 3**

# Simple and Complete Subjects and Predicates

In a sentence, the **simple subject** is the key word or words in the subject. The simple subject is usually a noun or a pronoun and does not include any modifiers. The **complete subject** includes the simple subject and all the words that modify it.

The **simple predicate** is the key verb that tells what the subject does, has, or is. The **complete predicate** includes the verb and all the words that modify it.

In the following sentence, a vertical line separates the complete subject and complete predicate. The simple subject is underlined once. The simple predicate is underlined twice.

> EXAMPLE
> **(complete subject)**        **(complete predicate)**
> The worn leather <u>pouch</u> | <u>contained</u> an iron shell, a pebble, and a sprig of sacred sage.

Sometimes, the simple subject is also the complete subject, and the simple predicate or verb is also the complete predicate.

> EXAMPLE
> <u>John Steinbeck</u> | <u>died</u>.

To find the simple subject and simple predicate in a sentence, first break the sentence into its two basic parts: complete subject and complete predicate. Then, identify the simple predicate by asking yourself, "What is the action of this sentence?" Then, identify the simple subject by asking yourself, "Who or what is performing the action?"

In the following sentences, the complete predicate is in brackets. The simple predicate, or verb, appears in boldface. Remember, verbs may have more than one word, and as many as four.

> EXAMPLES
> **one-word verb**      Two small chickadees
>                        [**shivered** on the snowy tree branch.]
> **two-word verb**      Two small chickadees
>                        [**are shivering** on the snowy tree branch.]
> **three-word verb**    Two small chickadees
>                        [**have been shivering** on the snowy tree branch.]
> **four-word verb**     Two small chickadees
>                        [**might have been shivering** on the snowy tree branch.]

# EXERCISE 1

## Identifying Simple and Complete Subjects and Predicates

Draw a vertical line between the complete subject and predicate in each sentence. Then, underline the simple subject once. Underline the simple predicate or verb twice.

EXAMPLE
The <u>people</u> in the ballroom | <u>are dancing</u> the flamenco.

1. An elderly man waits patiently at a corner table for his guest.

2. The young bugle boy proudly stood by the billowing flag.

3. The backyard birdfeeder has been attracting a variety of birds.

4. The mysterious guest might have been listening at the door.

5. A crowd of people blocked the exit doors.

6. Maria is making a long-distance phone call.

7. The lighthouse on the wharf shines its beacon brightly.

8. Two chocolate cupcakes are missing from the platter.

9. A new museum for American art will be built next spring.

10. The president's speech was heard by millions of people.

## EXERCISE 2

## Understanding Simple and Complete Subjects and Predicates

Each of the following sentences contains a simple subject and predicate. Revise each sentence by adding details to the simple subject and predicate to create a more specific and clear sentence. Then draw a vertical line between the complete subject and predicate you've created. Underline the original simple subject once. Underline the original simple predicate twice.

EXAMPLE
The dogs slept.
(The three black <u>dogs</u> | <u>slept</u> soundly through the storm.)

1. The boy laughed.

_____

2. A dancer is twirling.

_____

3. The team won.

_____

4. The roof has been leaking.

_____

5. A branch snapped.

_____

## EXERCISE 3

### Understanding Simple and Complete Subjects and Predicates

Each of the following sentences contains a complete subject and predicate. Draw a vertical line between the complete subject and predicate. Underline the simple subject once. Underline the simple predicate twice. Then simplify the sentence so that it contains only a simple subject and predicate.

> EXAMPLE
> Later that night, <u>Miss Kinnian</u> | <u>arrived</u> at the laboratory.
> (Miss Kinnian arrived.)

1. The doctors had been studying Charlie's intelligence for a long time.

_____

2. Charlie worried about taking the ink-blot test.

_____

3. Algernon quickly completed the difficult and confusing maze.

_____

4. The other workers at the factory signed a petition to have Charlie fired.

_____

5. Mrs. Flynn was knocking on the door of Charlie's apartment.

_____

## EXERCISE 4

### Using Simple and Complete Subjects and Predicates in Your Writing

Write a tall tale about a folk hero, such as Paul Bunyan, John Henry, or Annie Christmas. Add details to simple subjects and predicates to help your readers visualize the subject and the action that is taking place in the tale. Use your own sheet of paper for this exercise.

**LESSON 4**

# Compound Subjects, Compound Predicates, and Compound Sentences

A sentence may have more than one subject or predicate. A **compound subject** has two or more simple subjects that have the same predicate. The subjects are joined by the conjunction *and, or,* or *but*. A **compound predicate** has two or more simple predicates, or verbs, that share the same subject. The verbs are connected by the conjunction *and, or,* or *but*.

EXAMPLES
**compound subject**
Conflict and climax | occur in most short stories.

**compound predicate**
Many people | read short stories and enjoy them.

The conjunctions *neither* and *nor* can also join compound subjects and predicates.

EXAMPLES
**compound subject**
*Neither* Henry *nor* I | know the answer.

**compound predicate**
She | *neither* ran *nor* danced.

A sentence may have both a compound subject and a compound predicate.

EXAMPLE
**compound subject and compound predicate**
Greg and his father | sat down and talked about Greg's grades.

A **compound sentence** consists of at least two independent clauses joined by a semicolon or by a coordinating conjunction and a comma. Each part of the compound sentence has its own subject and verb. The most common coordinating conjunctions are *and, or, nor, for, but, so,* and *yet*.

EXAMPLES
**compound sentence**
Walter Dean Myers was born in West Virginia**;** he moved to Harlem at an early age.

**compound sentence**
Walter Dean Myers has been writing since childhood, **and** he has received many awards for his pieces of literature.

# EXERCISE 1

## Identifying Compound Subjects, Compound Predicates, and Compound Sentences

In each of the following sentences, underline all of the simple subjects once, and underline all of the simple predicates twice. Then tell whether the sentence has a compound subject, compound predicate, or compound subject and predicate, and whether the sentence is a compound sentence.

EXAMPLE
Greg and his father had a disagreement, so Greg left the house.
(compound subject, compound sentence)

1. Greg walked down the block and stopped at an abandoned building.

   _____

2. Greg sat on the couch and watched the stoplight change; he heard a scraping sound and listened carefully.

   _____

3. The wind and the rain shook the glass in the window.

   _____

4. Greg and Lemon Brown met in the dark room, and Lemon Brown threatened Greg.

   _____

5. Lemon Brown had traveled through Mississippi and sung the blues.

   _____

6. The three thugs were outside, yet Lemon Brown was scared of them.

   _____

7. The man banged the pipe against the banister and slowly walked up the stairs.

   _____

8. Greg and Lemon Brown had successfully scared the intruders away.

   _____

9. Lemon Brown's treasure is special to him and reminds him of his past.

   _____

10. Greg learns an important lesson; his father has set good goals for him.

    _____

*Writing & Grammar*

# EXERCISE 2

## Understanding Compound Subjects, Compound Predicates, and Compound Sentences

Write sentences containing the elements described in each of the directions below.

1. compound subject

   _____

   _____

2. compound predicate

   _____

   _____

3. compound subject and compound predicate

   _____

   _____

4. compound sentence using conjunction *and*

   _____

   _____

5. compound sentence using conjunction *but*

   _____

   _____

6. compound sentence using conjunction *so*

   _____

   _____

7. compound sentence using semicolon

   _____

   _____

8. compound subject and compound sentence

   _____

   _____

9. compound predicate and compound sentence

_____

_____

10. compound subject, compound predicate, and compound sentence

_____

_____

## EXERCISE 3

### Using Compound Subjects, Compound Predicates, and Compound Sentences in Your Writing

Write the opening scene to a short story or novel. Keep in mind that you'll need to establish the setting, introduce characters, and set up the story's conflict. Include in your opening scene five of the different combinations of compound elements listed in Exercise 2. Use your own sheet of paper for this exercise.

**LESSON 5**

# Identifying the Parts of Speech

Each word in a sentence performs a basic function or task. Words perform four basic tasks: they name, modify, express action or state of being, or connect. By the arrangement of words in a sentence and the task that each word performs within a sentence, you can understand a sentence's meaning. To illustrate how parts of speech work together, try to decipher the following nonsense sentence.

EXAMPLE
The avile and gharmy pillums stregged around a blarmy porgebout.

What nonsense noun is the subject of the sentence? What adjectives modify the word *pillums*? Which nonsense verb expresses the action in the sentence? If you substitute real words for the nonsense words, but keep the same arrangement of words, you can identify the nouns, verb, and adjectives in the sentence.

EXAMPLE
The brown and gray chipmunks gathered around a bubbling downspout.

There are eight basic parts of speech. Each part of speech is defined in the following chart.

| Part of Speech | Definition |
|---|---|
| **noun** | A **noun** names a person, place, thing, or idea. |
| **pronoun** | A **pronoun** is used in place of a noun. |
| **verb** | A **verb** expresses action or a state of being. |
| **adjective** | An **adjective** modifies a noun or pronoun. The most common adjectives are the articles *a*, *an*, and *the*. |
| **adverb** | An **adverb** modifies a verb, an adjective, or another adverb. |
| **preposition** | A **preposition** shows the relationship between its object—a noun or a pronoun—and another word in a sentence. Common prepositions include *after, around, at, behind, beside, off, through, until, upon,* and *with*. |
| **conjunction** | A **conjunction** joins words or groups of words. Common conjunctions are *and, but, for, nor, or, so,* and *yet*. |
| **interjection** | An **interjection** is a word used to express emotion. Common interjections are *oh, ah, well, hey,* and *wow*. |

EXAMPLES

| | |
|---|---|
| **noun** | **Soldiers** slept in their **uniforms**, waiting with **fear** for the next **battle**. |
| **pronoun** | Max whistled as **he** helped **his** dad paint **their** house. |
| **verb** | The sudden winds **snapped** tree limbs, **broke** power lines, and **caused** havoc. |
| **adjective** | In the **chipped blue** vase she put a **cheerful** bouquet of daisies and zinnias. |
| **adverb** | Holly jumped **quickly** into the pool, **nearly** landing on the raft. |
| **preposition** | **At** the base **of** the tree, poppies and wild violets grew **among** the ferns. |
| **conjunction** | **Neither** Felix **nor** Phillip arrived on time, **but** they apologized to the host. |
| **interjection** | **Hey!** You're wearing my new red sweater! |

# EXERCISE 1

## Identifying the Parts of Speech in Literature

Identify the part of speech of each underlined word in the following excerpt. Write your answers on the corresponding lines below.

¹Greg ²had sat in the small, pale-³green kitchen listening, knowing the lecture would end with ⁴his father saying he couldn't play ball ⁵with the Scorpions. He ⁶had asked his father the week before, ⁷and his father had said ⁸it depended ⁹on his next ¹⁰report card. It wasn't ¹¹often the Scorpions took on ¹²new players, ¹³especially fourteen-year-olds, and ¹⁴this was a chance of a ¹⁵lifetime for Greg. He ¹⁶hadn't been allowed to play high school ball, which he had ¹⁷really wanted to do, ¹⁸but playing ¹⁹for the Community Center team was ²⁰the next best thing.

*from "The Treasure of Lemon Brown," page 16*
*Walter Dean Myers*

1. _____    11. _____

2. _____    12. _____

3. _____    13. _____

4. _____    14. _____

5. _____    15. _____

6. _____    16. _____

7. _____    17. _____

8. _____    18. _____

9. _____    19. _____

10. _____    20. _____

*Writing & Grammar*

# EXERCISE 2

## Understanding the Parts of Speech

Use each word and its designated part of speech in a sentence.

EXAMPLES
fried (verb) Liam fried the eggs in a cast-iron skillet.
fried (adjective) He ate two fried eggs and whole wheat toast for breakfast.

1. them (pronoun)

   _____

2. hope (noun)

   _____

3. hope (verb)

   _____

4. delicately (adverb)

   _____

5. underneath (preposition)

   _____

6. but (conjunction)

   _____

7. oh (interjection)

   _____

8. alert (adjective)

   _____

9. friendly (adjective)

   _____

10. painting (noun)

    _____

## EXERCISE 3

### Using the Parts of Speech in Your Writing

Write a paragraph to a friend, in which you describe a real or imaginary surprise party. Include in your paragraph at least two examples of each part of speech.

_____

_____

_____

_____

_____

_____

_____

_____

_____

**LESSON 6**

# Common and Proper Nouns

A **noun** is a part of speech that names a person, place, idea, or thing. In this unit, you'll learn about the different kinds of nouns and what they name.

EXAMPLES
**people**    Dylan, principal, father, choreographer
**places**    home, Central Park, Joe's Tacos
**ideas**     love, multiplication, surprise, thought
**things**    basketball, dance, orbit, trading card

## Types of Nouns

| Type of Noun | Definition | Examples |
|---|---|---|
| **common noun** | names a person, place, idea, or thing | father, home, thought, table |
| **proper noun** | names a *specific* person, place, or thing; begins with capital letter | Lincoln, Gettysburg, Emancipation Proclamation |
| **concrete noun** | names a thing that can be touched, seen, heard, smelled, or tasted | notebook, face, song, scream, plum |
| **abstract noun** | names an idea, a quality, a concept, or a feeling | fantasy, psychology, Romanticism, hope |
| **singular noun** | names one person, place, idea, or thing | principal, park, feeling, chair |
| **plural noun** | names more than one thing | principals, parks, feelings, chairs |
| **possessive noun** | shows ownership or possession of things or qualities | Karl's, Mr. Poloni's, children's, nurse's |
| **compound noun** | made up of two or more words | grandmother, lemon tree, sister-in-law |
| **collective noun** | names groups | family, committee, class |

## Definition

The two basic kinds of nouns are *proper nouns* and *common nouns*. A **common noun** names *any* person, place, thing, or idea. Common nouns are usually not capitalized.

EXAMPLES
**common nouns**
**any person**   An **investigator** will soon arrive at the scene.
**any place**   The **river** crested earlier than usual this spring.
**any thing**   A **camera** records images on film.
**any idea**   The **thought** of writing twenty pages is overwhelming.

A **proper noun** names a *specific* person, place, or thing, and begins with a capital letter.

EXAMPLES
**common nouns**   student, monument, battle
**proper nouns**   Tom, Washington Monument, Battle of Shiloh

# EXERCISE 1

## Identifying Common and Proper Nouns in Literature

Identify the underlined nouns in the passage below as either common or proper.
Write your answers on the corresponding lines below.

What is that? ¹Faustin asked. There was an object with ²smoke coming from it. It was standing upright.
³Men are going to the ⁴moon, Nana, his grandson said. It's ⁵Apollo. It's going to fly three men to the moon.
That ⁶thing is going to fly to the moon?
Yes, ⁷Nana.
What is it called again?
Apollo, a spaceship ⁸rocket, ⁹Joselita told her father.
The Apollo spaceship stood on the ground emitting ¹⁰clouds of something that looked like smoke.

*from "Men on the Moon," page 123*
*Simon Ortiz*

1. _____   6. _____

2. _____   7. _____

3. _____   8. _____

4. _____   9. _____

5. _____   10. _____

# EXERCISE 2

## Understanding Common and Proper Nouns

For each of the following common nouns, write two proper nouns.

EXAMPLE
newspaper (*The New York Times, The Times-Picayune*)

1. magazine _____     _____

2. athlete _____     _____

3. continent _____     _____

4. planet _____     _____

5. actor _____     _____

6. relative _____     _____

7. author _____     _____

8. river _____     _____

9. city _____     _____

10. singer _____     _____

11. state _____     _____

12. country _____     _____

13. mountain _____     _____

14. politician _____     _____

15. teacher _____     _____

16. county _____     _____

17. school _____     _____

18. church _____     _____

19. book _____     _____

20. doctor _____     _____

# EXERCISE 3

## Using Common and Proper Nouns in Your Writing

Write a paragraph describing the town in which you live, including some of the specific sites of interest. Underline and label five common nouns and five proper nouns in your description. Notice how the use of proper nouns helps to make your description more specific.

_____

_____

_____

_____

_____

_____

_____

_____

_____

**LESSON 7**

# Singular and Plural Nouns

Nouns that represent one person, place, idea, or thing are called **singular nouns**. Most nouns that represent more than one person, place, idea, or thing are called **plural nouns**.

Most nouns are made plural by adding –*s* at the end. A few nouns have the same form in the singular and plural, and some nouns have irregular plural forms. The spelling of some nouns changes in the plural, depending on how the word ends.

EXAMPLES
**plural nouns**
For most nouns, to form the plural add –*s* to the end of the word.

shelter → shelters        piano → pianos
essay → essays            proof → proofs

If a noun ends in *s, sh, ch, x,* or *z,* add –*es.*
glass → glasses           wish → wishes
watch → watches           box → boxes
waltz → waltzes

If a noun ends in *o* preceded by a consonant, add –*es.*
tomato → tomatoes     potato → potatoes     echo → echoes

If a noun ends in *y* preceded by a consonant, change the *y* to *i* and add –*es.*
folly → follies       puppy → puppies       fairy → fairies

For some nouns that end in *f* or *fe,* change the *f* to *v* and add –*es* or –*s.*
leaf → leaves       shelf → shelves       wife → wives

# EXERCISE 1

## Identifying Singular and Plural Nouns in Literature

Underline the nouns in the following passage. Above each noun, write whether it is singular or plural.

The girls returned and instantly snapped into the dance. Their parasols opened

and twirling, they leaped over imaginary puddles and worried about their slippers.

They looked up at the sky, their hands out to see if the rain was falling. Their faces

bright with smiles they twirled their parasols with happy abandonment.

*from "Miss Butterfly," page E58*
*Toshio Mori*

# EXERCISE 2

## Correcting Singular and Plural Nouns

For each singular noun in items 1–10, write the correct plural form. In items 11–20 correct any error in the plural nouns listed. Write *correct* if the plural form is correct.

1.  painter _____
2.  brush _____
3.  soprano _____
4.  hero _____
5.  story _____
6.  baby _____
7.  self _____
8.  leaf _____
9.  belief _____
10. moose _____

11. attitudes _____
12. coachs _____
13. vetos _____
14. librarys _____
15. thiefs _____
16. halfs _____
17. trout _____
18. mouses _____
19. oxes _____
20. fishes _____

# EXERCISE 3

## Using Singular and Plural Nouns in Your Writing

Write a paragraph about the first day of school. Use at least five singular and five plural nouns.

_____
_____
_____
_____
_____
_____
_____
_____

*Writing & Grammar*

**LESSON 8**

# Possessive Nouns

Nouns that show ownership or possession of things or qualities are called **possessive nouns**. A possessive noun names who or what has something. Possessive nouns can also be singular or plural.

Both common nouns and proper nouns can be possessive in form.

EXAMPLES
**common nouns**
The **document's** pages were brittle and worn.
The **teachers'** conference started at nine o'clock.

**proper nouns**
**Maria's** flute needs polishing.
**America's** revolution against England inspired the French Revolution.

An apostrophe is used to form the possessive of nouns. To form the possessive of a singular noun, add an apostrophe and an *s* to the end of the word.

EXAMPLES
**singular possessive nouns**
**Karl's** Saturday job is in a restaurant. (Karl + 's = Karl's)
**Mr. Poloni's** hair is turning white. (Poloni + 's = Poloni's)

The possessive of a plural noun is formed two different ways. If the plural noun does not end in *s*, you add an apostrophe and an *s* to the end of the word. If the plural noun ends with an *s*, add only an apostrophe.

EXAMPLES
**plural possessive nouns**
**Children's** noses grow faster than the other parts of their faces.
   (Children + 's = Children's)
The **nurses'** job is to care for the patient. (nurses + ' = nurses')

## EXERCISE 1

### Identifying Possessive Nouns

Indicate whether the underlined nouns in the following sentences are plural, possessive, or both plural and possessive.

1. José's fingernails were full of grime, and his skin was calloused.

_____

2. José's <u>parents </u>worked hard to earn a living.

_____

3. His <u>cousin's </u>clothes and shoes were new and fashionable.

_____

4. There were <u>agencies</u> that found people jobs and took a portion of the pay.

_____

5. José learned to ignore the <u>comments</u> Arnie muttered as he worked.

_____

6. The <u>boys'</u> job was to spray-paint lawn furniture.

_____

7. As José and Arnie walked around to the backyard, Mr. <u>Clemens's</u> poodle was yapping.

_____

8. The <u>cousins</u> were in business together and split the profits eighty-twenty.

_____

9. José diligently cleaned the <u>pool's</u> algae and grime

_____

10. <u>José's</u> realization was that there are some people like Arnie, the liars, and there are some people who do the right thing, like himself.

_____

# EXERCISE 2

## Understanding How to Form Possessive Nouns

Rewrite each word group below, using the correct possessive form of the first word in each group.

1. comet tail   _____

2. mother love   _____

3. women rights   _____

4. birds wings   _____

5. tiger tail   _____

6. Minnesota winters   _____

7. Lewis explorations   _____

8. story moral   _____

9. book cover   _____

10. cat pajamas   _____

11. Prince Charles sons   _____

12. Shakespeare plays   _____

13. country population   _____

14. athletes records   _____

15. people jobs   _____

16. animals habitats   _____

17. sheep wool   _____

18. Maria sister   _____

19. men clothing   _____

20. seasons changes   _____

# EXERCISE 3

## Using Possessive Nouns

For each sentence write the correct possessive form of the underlined noun.

1. Between 250,000 and 420,000 boy soldiers served in the Union's and <u>Confederacy</u> armies.

   _____

2. The <u>soldiers</u> experience in battle is similar to reports by contemporary child soldiers in the Middle East.

   _____

3. The boys wanted to defend their <u>families</u> homes against an invading army.

   _____

4. Many parents supported the <u>boys</u> decision to enlist.

   _____

5. William <u>Bircher</u> sixteenth birthday had not yet arrived when he put on his blue uniform.

   _____

6. Sixteen-year-old Albert Blocker became one of the Third Texas <u>Cavalry</u> musicians.

   _____

7. Over forty thousand drummer boys served in the Union <u>Army</u> nonfighting positions.

   _____

8. A drummer <u>boy</u> job was to render the calls of reveille, breakfast, assembly, and taps.

   _____

9. The Third Ohio Volunteer <u>Regiment</u> commander laughed when Johnny Clem offered his services.

   _____

10. Johnny drew a <u>soldier</u> pay of thirteen dollars a month.

    _____

*Writing & Grammar*

**LESSON 9**

# Compound and Collective Nouns

A **compound noun** is a noun made up of two or more words. Some compound nouns are written as one word, some as two or more words, and some as hyphenated words.

EXAMPLES
| | |
|---|---|
| **one word** | grandmother, desktop, bookcase |
| **two or more words** | Valentine's Day, New York, lemon tree, mother of the bride |
| **hyphenated** | sister-in-law, twelve-year-old, great-grandfather |

Most compound nouns form their plurals by adding *s* or *es* at the end. In other cases, when one part of the compound noun is modified by another part, they add an *s* or *es* to the part that is modified.

## EXERCISE 1

### Identifying Compound Nouns

Identify the compound nouns in the following sentences.

1. My brother Evan is a marine biologist.

   _____

2. I met my brother-in-law for the first time at the wedding.

   _____

3. Franklin hoped to be promoted to vice president one day.

   _____

4. My favorite place to read is on the couch in the living room.

   _____

5. Many people are afraid to work in the upper stories of a skyscraper.

   _____

6. There is much superstition associated with the full moon.

   _____

7. The runner-up in the contest made a persuasive speech.

_____

8. Kevin set the bowl of sweet potatoes on the table in the dining room.

_____

9. My younger sister is an eighth-grader this year and likes her homeroom.

_____

10. Frederick won the freestyle competition at yesterday's meet.

_____

11. The ring's gemstones sparkled in the sunlight.

_____

12. My roommate was from New York.

_____

13. Colin Powell is the first African American to become Secretary of State.

_____

14. Many of my most treasured T-shirts are hand-me-downs.

_____

15. The caddy brought a twelve-pack of soda to the golf club.

_____

16. The attorney general is appointed by the president.

_____

17. The value of real estate has increased rapidly in our neighborhood.

_____

18. Most families belong to the middle class.

_____

19. My brother wants to join the Air Force to become a pilot.

_____

20. Our grandmother went with us to the swimming pool.

_____

# EXERCISE 2

## Understanding Plural Compound Nouns

Use the plural form of the compound noun in parentheses to complete each sentence. You may need to use a dictionary to check your answers.

1. The children kept their (storybook) on the shelf.

   _____

2. All the (runner-up) stood together on the stage.

   _____

3. Did you know Annie has two (great-grandmother)?

   _____

4. Several of the (music box) hadn't been opened in years.

   _____

5. The new (father-in-law) met and shook hands.

   _____

6. The previous (attorney general) worked in the federal building.

   _____

7. At the gallery, the (printmaker) displayed their latest work.

   _____

8. Refrigerators used to be called (ice box).

   _____

9. (Iceberg) are massive floating bodies of ice broken from a glacier.

   _____

10. Let's order chocolate (ice-cream soda).

    _____

# EXERCISE 3

## Using Compound Nouns

Write a sentence using each of the compound nouns listed below.

1. fourteen-year-old

   _____

   _____

2. makeup

   _____

   _____

3. mass-production

   _____

   _____

4. keyboard

   _____

   _____

5. post office

   _____

   _____

6. half brother

   _____

   _____

7. football

   _____

   _____

8. editors in chief

   _____

   _____

*Writing & Grammar*

9. bull's eye

_____

_____

10. maids of honor

_____

_____

# Collective Nouns

**Collective nouns**—such as *family, committee,* and *class*—name groups that are made up of individuals. A collective noun may be either singular or plural, depending on how the group acts. When the group acts together as one unit to do something, the group is considered *singular.* When individuals within the group act differently or do different things at the same time, the collective noun is *plural.*

EXAMPLES
**singular**    The **committee** votes on its agenda.
        The **family** enjoys old movies.
**plural**     The **committee** were giving their reports.
        The **family** disagree about what to rent at the video store.

## EXERCISE 4

### Identifying Collective Nouns

Underline the five collective nouns in the following paragraph.

We watched a documentary about African elephants. The program showed a

herd of elephants working together to raise the young members of their family.

Sometimes a pack of hyenas can threaten and even kill a large elephant. The

crew filming the documentary shot terrific footage of animals on the African

plains. The film illustrated how varied the animal population of Africa truly is.

## EXERCISE 5

### Understanding Collective Noun-Verb Agreement

Underline the collective noun in each of the following sentences. Then rewrite the sentence using the correct form of the verb in parentheses.

1. After listening to evidence, the jury (decides, decide) its verdict.

   _____

2. Our drama club (raises, raise) money by selling popcorn.

   _____

3. The flock of geese (quarrels, quarrel) among themselves over the breadcrumbs.

   _____

4. A swarm of ants (crawls, crawl) over the picnic table.

   _____

5. The orchestra (practices, practice) their separate parts before the concert.

   _____

6. A choir (includes, include) sopranos, tenors, altos, and baritones.

   _____

7. After the team (gets, get) individual assignments, they head outside for drills.

   _____

8. The newborn litter of kittens (looks, look) adorable.

   _____

9. The editorial staff (works, work) on different articles.

   _____

10. A pod of whales (swims, swim) with the ocean current.

    _____

## EXERCISE 6

### Using Collective Nouns in Your Writing

Write a paragraph about one of the following groups: club, crew, team, troop, or a group of your own choosing. Describe the group and its activities, using a collective noun as a singular subject at least twice and as a plural subject at least twice.

_____

_____

_____

_____

*Writing & Grammar*

**LESSON 10**

# Pronouns

A **pronoun** is used in place of a noun. Sometimes a pronoun refers to a specific person or thing.

Pronouns can help your writing flow more smoothly. Without pronouns, your writing can sound awkward and repetitive. Take a look at the following examples, which show the same sentence written without and with pronouns.

EXAMPLES

**without pronouns**    Derrick discussed **Derrick's** idea and **Derrick's** plan for the recycling program and presented **the idea and plan** to the committee.

**with pronouns**    Derrick discussed **his** idea and **his** plan for the recycling program and presented **them** to the committee.

The most commonly used pronouns are *personal pronouns, reflexive* and *intensive pronouns, demonstrative pronouns, indefinite pronouns, interrogative pronouns,* and *relative pronouns.*

## Types of Pronouns

| Type of Pronoun | Definition | Examples |
|---|---|---|
| **personal pronoun** | used in place of the name of a person or thing | I, me, we, us, he, she, it, him, her, you, they, them, my, mine, your, yours, his, hers, our, ours, their, theirs |
| **indefinite pronoun** | points out a person, place, or thing, but not a specific or definite one | one, someone, anything, other, all, few, nobody |
| **reflexive pronoun** | refers back to a noun previously used; adds *–self* and *–selves* to other pronoun forms | myself, herself, himself, itself, yourself, themselves, ourselves |
| **intensive pronoun** | emphasizes a noun or pronoun | I *myself*, she *herself*, he *himself*, it *itself*, you *yourself*, they *themselves*, we *ourselves* |
| **interrogative pronoun** | asks a question | who, whose, whom, what, which |
| **demonstrative pronoun** | points out a specific person, place, idea, or thing | this, these, that, those |
| **relative pronoun** | introduces an adjective clause | that, which, who, whose, whom |

# Personal Pronoun

A **personal pronoun** is used in place of the name of a person or thing. Personal pronouns are singular, plural, or possessive.

| Type of Pronoun | Definition | Examples |
|---|---|---|
| **singular pronoun** | used in place of the name of one person or thing | I, me, you, he, she, it, him, her |
| **plural pronoun** | used in place of more than one person or thing | we, us, you, they, them |
| **possessive pronoun** | shows ownership or possession | my, mine, your, yours, his, her, hers, our, ours, their, theirs |

Use personal pronouns to refer to yourself (first person), to refer to people to whom you are talking (second person), and to refer to other people, places, and things (third person).

EXAMPLES

**first person**    the speaker or speakers talk about themselves: *I, me, my, mine, we, us, our, ours*

**second person**   the speaker talks about the person talked to: *you, your, yours*

**third person**    the speaker talks about someone or something else: *he, him, his, she, her, hers, it, its, they, them, their, theirs*

## EXERCISE 1

### Identifying Pronouns in Literature

Underline the eleven pronouns in the following passage.

Grandpa relaxed, and between sips of soup, he told us of his journey. Soon

after our visit to him, Grandpa decided that he would like to see where his only

living descendants lived and what our home was like. Besides, he admitted

sheepishly, he was lonesome after we left.

*from "The Medicine Bag," page E66*
*Virginia Driving Hawk Sneve*

## EXERCISE 2

### Understanding Pronouns

Rewrite each of the following sentences or sentence pairs. Use pronouns in place of any repetitive nouns or groups of nouns.

1. Kim and Mike went to the local art museum. Kim and Mike really enjoyed the local art museum.

   _____

   _____

2. Now Mike wants Kim to help Mike paint a mural. Mike thinks Kim is a good artist.

   _____

   _____

3. Ms. Chang said that Mike and Kim could use Ms. Chang's garage door as Mike and Kim's canvas.

   _____

   _____

4. On Saturday the two friends started the job. The two friends realized that the job would take the two friends a number of weekends to complete.

   _____

   _____

5. Kim told Kim's father that Kim would need a ladder. Kim's father brought Kim's father's ladder to Ms. Chang's house.

   _____

   _____

6. Maria and I stopped by to see the mural. Maria and I asked Kim and Mike, "Is the mural design Kim and Mike's?"

   _____

   _____

7. "Yes," Mike said, "The design is Kim and Mike's."

   _____

   _____

8. Maria asked Kim and Mike: "Do Kim and Mike want to take a break?" Maria wanted Kim and Mike to go with Maria to a movie.

_____

_____

9. Ms. Chang liked the mural's colors. The mural's bright greens and blues would cheer up the neighborhood.

_____

_____

10. The young painters congratulated the young painters for a job well done.

_____

_____

## EXERCISE 3

### Using Pronouns in Your Writing

Write a paragraph that describes a suspenseful scene. Begin your paragraph with this sentence: "The cloaked stranger slowly opened the castle's massive door." Use at least five different pronouns in your descriptive paragraph.

_____

_____

_____

_____

_____

_____

_____

_____

_____

_____

_____

_____

**LESSON 11**

# Pronouns and Antecedents

As you know, a *pronoun* is a word used in place of one or more nouns. The word that a pronoun stands for is called its **antecedent**. The antecedent clarifies the meaning of the pronoun. The pronoun may appear in the same sentence as its antecedent or in a following sentence.

EXAMPLES
Is Maria here? Tony saw her come inside.
(*Maria* is the antecedent of *her.*)

My best friend lives in Chicago, and she visits in the summer.
(*My best friend* is the antecedent of *she.*)

## EXERCISE 1

### Identifying Pronouns and Antecedents

Identify the personal pronoun(s) in each of the following sentences or sentence pairs. Then identify the antecedent to which each pronoun refers.

1. Edgar Allan Poe was born in Boston, Massachusetts, and he had a brother and a sister.

   _____

2. Poe was taken in by the Allan family, and they traveled to England.

   _____

3. Poe's only completed novel is *The Narrative of Arthur Gordon Pym.* It was published in 1838.

   _____

4. Poe's collection of poetry *The Raven and Other Poems* gained him recognition; it contained the very successful poem, "The Raven."

   _____

5. Poe wrote many poems, and they were published in numerous magazines.

   _____

6. My best friend loves the story "The Tell-Tale Heart." She read it in class.

   _____

7. Poe published many works. Will the class read them?

   _____

8. The class studied the short story. It is about a confessed murderer.

   _____

9. Poe was a poet, short-story writer, and critic. He contributed to the genres of
   horror and science fiction.

   _____

10. Mrs. Alvarez read Poe's poems, and they deeply influenced her.

   _____

## EXERCISE 2

## Understanding Pronouns and Antecedents

In each blank write the correct pronoun. Then underline the pronoun's antecedent.

1. O. Henry is a highly acclaimed author. _____ wrote many
   short stories, including "The Ransom of Red Chief."

2. "The Ransom of Red Chief" is my favorite. _____ is an
   interesting and well-written story.

3. O. Henry's short stories are very popular. _____ have even
   been made into movies.

4. My sister recommended two other short stories. I'll read _____
   during summer vacation.

5. My friends Sarah and Josh like O. Henry's short stories, too. "The Ransom of

   Red Chief" is also _____ favorite.

6. Josh enjoyed the story's twist. The novel's characters also appealed to

   _____.

7. Sarah doesn't own many books. Josh often lends his books to

   _____.

8. Sarah, Josh, and I went to the library together last night. _____
   studied for the math test.

9. I couldn't carry all my books in the backpack. Josh offered to carry some of

   them for _____.

10. Sarah and I live on the same street. Josh kindly offered to walk

   _____ home.

## EXERCISE 3

### Using Pronouns and Antecedents in Your Writing

Write a brief review of a film you've seen recently. In your review, you might discuss such elements as plot, characters, and special effects. Use at least five different pronouns in your review. Check your review for correct pronoun-antecedent agreement. Then draw an arrow from each pronoun to the antecedent to which it refers.

_____

_____

_____

_____

_____

_____

_____

_____

_____

_____

_____

_____

_____

**LESSON 12**

# Subject and Object Pronouns

Personal pronouns are sometimes used as the subjects of sentences. Personal pronouns are also used as the objects of verbs or prepositions.

A **subject pronoun** is used as the subject of a sentence. An **object pronoun** is used as the object of a verb or a preposition.

EXAMPLES

| | |
|---|---|
| **subject pronoun** | Max enjoys winter sports. **He** especially likes snowboarding. (subject of sentence) |
| **object pronoun** | Snowboarding invigorates **him**. (direct object of the verb *invigorates*) |
| **object pronoun** | Max's father bought **him** a new snowboard. (indirect object of the verb *bought*) |
| **object pronoun** | Max lent the new snowboard to **me**. (object of the preposition *to*) |

| Personal Pronouns | | |
|---|---|---|
| | **Singular** | **Plural** |
| Used as subjects | I<br>you<br>he, she, it | we<br>you<br>they |
| Used as objects | me<br>you<br>him, her, it | us<br>you<br>them |

Subject and object pronouns are also used in compound subjects and compound objects.

EXAMPLES

Megan and Jacob recently read the story "Sweet Potato Pie."
**She** and **he** recently read the story "Sweet Potato Pie." (*She* and *he* form the compound subject.)

Many of the characters seemed interesting to Megan and Jacob.
Many of the characters seemed interesting to **her** and **him**. (*Her* and *him* form the compound object.)

Use the subject pronoun *I* and the object pronoun *me* last when they are part of the compound subject or object.

EXAMPLES
**compound subject**
incorrect    I and Lydia volunteered to organize the recycling project.
correct      **Lydia and I** volunteered to organize the recycling project.

**compound object**
incorrect    They asked me and Nick to help with the project.
correct      They asked **Nick and me** to help with the project.

# EXERCISE 1

## Identifying Subject and Object Pronouns in Literature

Identify each of the underlined words as either a *subject pronoun* or an *object pronoun*. Write your answers on the corresponding lines below.

[1]They gave [2]him the name *Iron Shell,* but neither did [3]they understand the meaning of the dream. The first Iron Shell kept the piece of iron with [4]him at all times and believed [5]it gave [6]him protection from the evils of those unhappy days.

*from "The Medicine Bag," page E66*
*Virginia Driving Hawk Sneve*

1. _____

2. _____

3. _____

4. _____

5. _____

6. _____

# EXERCISE 2

## Understanding Subject and Object Pronouns

Underline the correct subject or object pronoun(s) in parentheses to complete each sentence. Then identify each pronoun as either a subject pronoun or an object pronoun.

1. Michael and (I, me) identified with the main character in the story.

   _____

2. Sheila introduced (we, us) to her friends at the party.

   _____

3. Josh found the packages on the doorstep and carried (they, them) into the house.

   _____

4. For Patrick's birthday Kim gave (he, him) a CD.

   _____

5. Would you believe they elected (I, me) to the student council?

   _____

6. The judge presented a purple ribbon to (she, her).

   _____

7. (He, him) and (she, her) recently visited their cousins in Chicago.

   _____

8. Will (they, them) try out for the basketball or football team?

   _____

9. Please let (I, me) help you.

   _____

10. (She, Her) went with (we, us) to the evening concert.

    _____

## EXERCISE 3

## Using Subject and Object Pronouns in Your Writing

Write a paragraph about an adventure or humorous event that you experienced with a friend. Correctly use subject and object pronouns in the paragraph.

_____

_____

_____

_____

_____

**LESSON 13**

# Possessive Pronouns

A **possessive pronoun** is a kind of pronoun that shows who or what has something. Possessive pronouns have two forms. When a possessive pronoun stands alone, it acts as a pronoun. When a possessive pronoun is used before a noun, it acts as an adjective.

EXAMPLES

**used alone**      The red house on the corner is **ours**.
             The purple mittens are **mine**.
             **Yours** have blue and white stripes.

**used before nouns**   Will you bring **my** backpack?
             Harriet will enter **her** experiment in the science fair.
             **Their** assignments were written on the board.

## Possessive Pronouns

|                     | **Singular**              | **Plural**              |
| ------------------- | ------------------------- | ----------------------- |
| **Used alone**      | mine<br>yours<br>hers, his, its | ours<br>yours<br>theirs |
| **Used as adjectives** | my<br>your<br>her, his, its | our<br>your<br>their |

## EXERCISE 1

### Identifying Possessive Pronouns in Literature

Underline the possessive pronouns in the following passage.

Moon's mother remembered when her second son had gone off to college the

year before. "It's difficult to let go, but it's much worse to hold on," she had said

to Moon's father, and Moon, listening nearby, had suddenly and unaccountably

run up to his room and slammed his door shut with such force that, to the

disquiet of his father, the paint cracked near the ceiling on the hallway wall. She now gazed sadly at her youngest son, so different from the ambitious older

ones: Andrew in engineering and football; Colin in pre-med and crew. And

Morgan—so edgy and sullen, so fixed upon himself.

*from "Moon," page 134*
*Chaim Potok*

## EXERCISE 2

## Understanding Possessive Pronouns

Write a sentence using each of the following possessive pronouns.

1. my

_____

2. your

_____

3. her (used before a noun)

_____

4. its (used before a noun)

_____

5 our

_____

6. their

_____

7. mine

_____

8. his (used alone)

_____

9. yours

_____

10. theirs

_____

*Writing & Grammar*

# EXERCISE 3

## Using Possessive Pronouns in Your Writing

Write a paragraph describing an object or possession that holds special meaning for you. Use at least five different possessive pronouns in your paragraph.

_____

_____

_____

_____

_____

_____

_____

_____

_____

_____

_____

_____

_____

**LESSON 14**

# Indefinite Pronouns

An **indefinite pronoun** points out a person, place, or thing, but not a particular or definite one. The chart below lists indefinite pronouns.

| Singular | | Plural |
|---|---|---|
| someone | everything | many |
| somebody | another | few |
| something | either | both |
| anyone | neither | several |
| anybody | each | others |
| anything | one | |
| everyone | nobody | |
| everybody | nothing | |

EXAMPLES
**Everything** about computers is a mystery to me.
**Someone** drank the last carton of milk.

Don't be confused if a phrase comes between an indefinite pronoun and the verb in a sentence. When an indefinite pronoun is the subject of a sentence, it must agree in number with the verb. However, the indefinite pronouns *all, any, more, most, none,* and *some* can be singular or plural.

EXAMPLES
**Most** of the garden **blooms** in early summer. (singular)
**Most** of the flowers **bloom** in early summer. (plural)

# EXERCISE 1

## Identifying Indefinite Pronouns

Underline the indefinite pronouns in the following sentences.

1. On the mural project, many of the students were without previous art experience.

2. The student interns learned something about painting from the mentor artists.

3. In Minneapolis, Minnesota, nearly everyone knows about the *Language of Hope* mural.

4. Each of the interns studied the visual elements of line, color, and composition.

5. Talking about the mural, one of the students said that it illustrated the meaning of respect for others.

6. Some of the symbols and images contradicted the students' perspectives of their culture.

7. Several of the interns identified values that they felt were essential to human life.

8. All of the teens learned that art was a fundamental human activity.

9. It was a rewarding experience for most of the interns and the mentor artists.

10. A college education was once a privilege available to only a few.

## EXERCISE 2

## Understanding Indefinite Pronouns

Identify the indefinite pronoun in each of the following sentences. Then choose the word or words in parentheses that correctly complete the sentence. Tell whether the indefinite pronoun is singular or plural.

EXAMPLE
Few of today's artists (achieves, achieve) success.
(*Few; achieve;* plural)

1. Others in the cast (dresses, dress) for the rehearsal.

   _____

   _____

   _____

2. At the sound of the bell, everyone in the classroom (gathers, gather) his or her books.

   _____

   _____

   _____

3. Most of the elephants (lives, live) in Africa and Asia.

   _____

   _____

   _____

4. Obviously, neither of the candidates (wants, want) to lose the election.

   _____

   _____

   _____

5. Hannah thinks some of the food dishes (tastes, taste) too spicy.

   _____

   _____

   _____

6. Many of the characters in the film (is, are) eccentric and funny.

   _____

   _____

   _____

7. Kevin said that all of his sisters (likes, like) to play basketball.

   _____

   _____

   _____

8. One of our friends (believes, believe) chocolate is good for her health.

   _____

   _____

   _____

9. Several of the horses (stays, stay) in the pasture during the day.

   _____

   _____

   _____

*Writing & Grammar*

10. None (volunteers, volunteer) his or her opinion about the book.

_____

_____

_____

## EXERCISE 3

## Using Indefinite Pronouns

Write ten sentences using the indefinite pronouns below.

1. either

_____

2. much

_____

3. nothing

_____

4. anybody

_____

5. none

_____

6. any

_____

7. everyone

_____

8. others

_____

9. neither

_____

10. many

_____

**LESSON 15**

# Action Verbs and State of Being Verbs

A **verb** is a word used to express action or a state of being. An **action verb** may express physical action or mental action. The action may or may not be one that you see—but, either way, an action verb tells you that something is happening, has happened, or will happen.

EXAMPLES

**physical action**    Their star hitter **smacks** the ball out of the park.
                       She quietly **tiptoed** down the hallway.
**mental action**      Finally, I **memorized** the long poem "The Highwayman."
                       Tom always **forgets** his keys on the counter.

A state of being verb does not tell about an action. A **state of being verb** tells you when and where someone or something exists. State of being verbs are formed from the verb *to be.*

## Forms of Be

| am | be | being | was | are | been | is | were |
|----|----|-------|-----|-----|------|----|------|

EXAMPLES
The spinach pizza **is** ready now.
Your grandparents **were** in town yesterday.

## EXERCISE 1

### Identifying Action Verbs and State of Being Verbs in Literature

Tell whether each of the underlined verbs is an action verb or a state of being verb. Write your answers on the corresponding lines below.

They ¹<u>were</u> flat round wafers, slightly browned on the edges and butter-yellow in the center. With the cold lemonade they were sufficient for childhood's lifelong diet. Remembering my manners, I ²<u>took</u> nice little lady-like bites off the edges. She ³<u>said</u> she had made them expressly for me and that she ⁴<u>had</u> a few in the kitchen that I could take home to my brother. So I ⁵<u>jammed</u> one whole cake in my mouth and the rough crumbs scratched the insides of my jaws, and if I hadn't had to swallow, it ⁶<u>would have been</u> a dream come true.

*from "Mrs. Flowers," page 177*
*Maya Angelou*

1. _____

2. _____

3. _____

4. _____

5. _____

6. _____

## EXERCISE 2

### Understanding Action Verbs and State of Being Verbs

Complete each of the following sentences. Include in the predicate an action verb or state of being verb, as indicated.

EXAMPLES
The marshmallows (state of being verb)
(The marshmallows **are** *on the roasting stick*)

A campfire (action verb)
(A campfire **glowed** *brightly in the distance.*)

1. The pioneer children (state of being verb)

   _____

2. A fat porcupine (action verb)

   _____

3. The children's father (state of being verb)

   _____

4. To survive, they (action verb)

   _____

5. An old blanket and lantern (state of being verb)

   _____

6. The one-horse wagon (action verb)

   _____

7. A snow-capped mountain (state of being verb)

   _____

8. Along the dusty trail (state of being verb)

   _____

9. The hungry child (action verb)

   _____

10. Their father's dark eyes (action verb)

    _____

## EXERCISE 3

### Using Action Verbs and State of Being Verbs in Your Writing

Imagine that you are on a journey. Your journey could take place in the present or in the past. Write a journal entry describing your experience. Use three different state of being verbs and three different action verbs in your description.

_____

_____

_____

_____

_____

_____

_____

_____

*Writing & Grammar*

**LESSON 16**

# Linking and Helping Verbs

## Linking Verbs

Like a state of being verb, a linking verb does not express an action. A **linking verb** links, or connects, the subject with a word or words in the predicate that describe or rename the subject.

> EXAMPLES
> The loaf of bread **was** moldy. (The verb *was* connects the subject *loaf* with a word that describes it—*moldy.*)
>
> The summer heat and humidity **are** unbearable. (The verb *are* connects the compound subject *heat and humidity* with a word that describes it— *unbearable.*)

Linking verbs can be formed from the verb *to be.*

> EXAMPLES

| am | be | being | was | are | been | is | were |
|----|----|-------|-----|-----|------|----|------|

The common linking verbs are listed below.

| Linking Verbs | | | |
|----|----|----|----|
| forms of *be* | feel | remain | sound |
| become | grow | seem | taste |
| appear | look | smell | |

> EXAMPLES
> The roast turkey **smells** delicious! (The linking verb *smells* connects the subject *turkey* with a word that describes the turkey—*delicious.*)
>
> Our coach **became** frustrated with the umpire. (The linking verb *became* connects the subject *coach* with a word that describes the coach—*frustrated.*)

Note that some linking verbs can also be used as action verbs.

EXAMPLES

| linking verb | They **remained** hopeful for his recovery. |
| action verb | Only one cookie **remained** on the plate. |
| linking verb | The bread in the oven **smelled** warm and spicy. |
| action verb | The bird dog **smelled** the ducks in the brush. |
| linking verb | Our 90-year-old grandmother still **looks** spry. |
| action verb | She **looks** at the rare stamp with a magnifying glass. |

# EXERCISE 1

## Identifying Linking Verbs in Literature

Underline the seven linking verbs in the following literature passage.

The language was a source of embarrassment. More times than not, I had tried

to disassociate myself from the nagging loud voice that followed me wherever

I wandered in the nearby American supermarket outside Chinatown. The voice

belonged to my grandmother, a fragile woman in her seventies who could

outshout the best of the street vendors. Her humor was raunchy, her Chinese

rhythmless, patternless. It was quick, it was loud, it was unbeautiful. It was

not like the quiet, lilting romance of French or the gentle refinement of the

American South. Chinese sounded pedestrian. Public.

*from "The Struggle to Be an All-American Girl," page 220*
*Elizabeth Wong*

# EXERCISE 2

## Understanding Linking Verbs

Use each of the following linking verbs in a sentence. If you wish, you may change
the form of the verbs.

EXAMPLE
was (form of be) (*He was always very kind and polite.*)

1. look

   _____

2. feel

   _____

3. appear

_____

4. sound

_____

5. grow

_____

6. become

_____

7. smell

_____

8. taste

_____

9. is (form of *be*)

_____

10. seem

_____

## EXERCISE 3

### Using Linking Verbs in Your Writing

Imagine that you have been granted one special wish. Write a paragraph describing
what happens when your wish is granted to you. Include each of the following verbs.
(You may include other verbs as well.) Use one of these verbs twice, once as an
action verb and once as a linking verb.

| appear | seem | become | feel | look |
|--------|------|--------|------|------|

_____

_____

_____

_____

# Helping Verbs

A **helping verb** helps the main verb to tell about an action. One or more helping verbs followed by a main verb is called a **verb phrase**. In the following examples, the verb phrases are underlined and the helping verbs appear in boldface.

EXAMPLES
I **am** taking dance lessons.
The dancers **will be** practicing a new routine today.
Our teacher **must have been** preparing for today's class.

The common helping verbs and their forms are listed in the following chart.

| Helping Verbs | | | |
|---|---|---|---|
| **Forms of *be*** | **Forms of *do*** | **Forms of *have*** | **Other helping verbs** |
| am        were<br>is          be<br>are        being<br>was       been | do<br>does<br>did | have<br>has<br>had | can        shall<br>could      should<br>may        will<br>might      would<br>must |

Sometimes helping verbs and main verbs are separated by other words.

EXAMPLES
I **did** not **clean** my room this weekend. (The helping verb *did* and the main verb *clean* are separated by the word *not*.)

The firefighters **had** clearly **exhausted** themselves. (The helping verb *had* and the main verb *exhausted* are separated by the word *clearly*.)

Note that some helping verbs can also be used as main verbs.

EXAMPLES
**main verb**        We **had** a visitor last night.
**helping verb**   A visitor **had arrived** on our doorstep.

Sometimes a helping verb becomes part of a contraction with a pronoun or a negative word.

EXAMPLES
I have been swimming a lot lately.
**I've** been swimming a lot lately.

She will be driving us to the airport.
**She'll** be driving us to the airport.

He does not know where you live.
He **doesn't** know where you live.

## EXERCISE 4

### Identifying Helping Verbs in Literature

Underline the seven verb phrases that contain a helping verb and a main verb in the following literature passage. Remember that a word or group of words might separate a helping verb and main verb.

In 1835, the padres of Mission Santa Barbara transferred the San Nicolas

Indians to the mainland. A few minutes after the boat, which was carrying

the Indians, had put off from the island, it was found that one baby had been

left behind. It is not easy to land a boat on San Nicolas; the captain decided

against returning for the baby; the baby's mother jumped overboard, and was

last seen swimming toward the island. Half-hearted efforts made to find her in

subsequent weeks were unsuccessful: it was believed that she had drowned in

the rough surf.

*from "Ishi in Two Worlds," page 186*
*Theodora Kroeber*

## EXERCISE 5

### Understanding Helping Verbs

Complete the following sentences by adding one or more helping verbs that fit the meaning. Then identify the complete verb phrase.

EXAMPLE
Theodora Kroeber _____ overwhelmed by the emotional response to Ishi's story.
(Theodora Kroeber <u>was overwhelmed</u> by the emotional response to Ishi's story.)

1. Ishi _____ found near the corral fence of a slaughter house.

   _____

2. The sheriff locked Ishi in a jail cell so he _____ at least protect him from the curiosity of the townspeople.

   _____

3. It was evident that Ishi _____

   _____ suffering because he was starved and fatigued.

   _____

4. Ishi _____ not eat or drink anything his first couple of days in captivity.

_____

5. Many of the local people _____ try to communicate with Ishi.

_____

6. The story of the capture of a "wild Indian" _____ reached the San Francisco newspapers.

_____

7. The stories _____ read by Professors Kroeber and Waterman, anthropologists at the University of California.

_____

8. Ishi _____ _____ been from the southernmost tribe of Yana.

_____

9. Waterman _____ finally say a word that Ishi recognizes.

_____

10. The information Ishi gave us _____

_____ used to better understand the Yahi culture.

_____

# EXERCISE 6

## Using Helping Verbs in Your Writing

Write a brief biography of a friend or family member. Describe important dates, events, people, and places in their life. Use at least five different helping verbs in your biography.

_____

_____

_____

_____

_____

*Writing & Grammar*

**LESSON 17**

# Transitive and Intransitive Verbs

An action verb that has a direct object is called a **transitive verb**. An action verb that does not have a direct object is called an **intransitive verb**.

EXAMPLES
**transitive verb**    Sally **put** the **seashell** on the windowsill.
(The seashell receives the action; therefore, it is the direct object of the transitive verb *put*.)

**intransitive verb**    The pink seashell **shimmered** in the sun.
(There is no direct object; therefore, *shimmered* is an intransitive verb.)

Don't confuse a direct object with an object of a preposition. A direct object never appears in a prepositional phrase.

EXAMPLES
**direct object of a verb**    Kristy poured the **water** into the glass.
**object of a preposition**    Kristy poured the water into the **glass**.

## EXERCISE 1

### Identifying Transitive and Intransitive Verbs in Literature

Identify the underlined verbs in the following literature passage as either transitive or intransitive. If a verb is transitive, identify its direct object. Write your answers on the corresponding lines below.

At ten o'clock we ¹set the table. For a centerpiece Mama ²put some pink and white sasanquas to float in a crystal bowl, and the low autumn light ³came slanting in through the windows onto the flowers and the bright water. We ⁴had built a fire in the stove, and the heat ⁵baked out the hay-field fragrance of the bunches of Artemisia hung to dry against the walls. The floors ⁶gleamed. The polished silverware ⁷shone. Beneath the sweet fall smells of baking bread and sasanquas and drying herbs I ⁸could just detect the faintest whiff of Murphy Oil Soap. Louise and I ⁹stood in the middle of the living room and ¹⁰gazed.

*from "Good Housekeeping," page E94*
*Bailey White*

1. _____    6. _____

2. _____    7. _____

3. _____    8. _____

4. _____    9. _____

5. _____    10. _____

## EXERCISE 2

## Understanding Transitive and Intransitive Verbs

Write a sentence using the transitive or intransitive verb indicated. Underline the verb. If the verb is transitive, then underline its direct object as well.

EXAMPLES
carried (transitive) (*The grandson* <u>carried</u> *the sacred* <u>sage</u> *in the medicine pouch.*)
walks (intransitive) (*Grandpa* <u>walks</u> *around the block every day.*)

1. shook (intransitive)

   _____

2. understand (transitive)

   _____

3. waited (intransitive)

   _____

4. are working (intransitive)

   _____

5. visits (transitive)

   _____

6. gave (transitive)

   _____

7. respect (transitive)

   _____

8. prepared (intransitive)

   _____

9. open (transitive)

_____

10. found (transitive)

_____

## EXERCISE 3

### Using Transitive and Intransitive Verbs in Your Writing

Write a descriptive paragraph about an object that holds special meaning in your family or heritage. Use at least three transitive verbs and three intransitive verbs in your paragraph.

_____

_____

_____

_____

_____

_____

_____

_____

_____

**LESSON 18**

# Verb Tenses

## The Simple Tenses

Verbs have different forms, called **tenses**, which are used to tell the time in which an action takes place. In your writing and speaking, you most commonly use the simple tenses. The **simple tenses** of the verb are **present**, **past**, and **future**.

The **present tense** tells that an action happens now—in the present time.

EXAMPLES

| | |
|---|---|
| **present tense singular** | The black crow **swoops** across the backyard. |
| **present tense plural** | The black crows **swoop** across the backyard. |
| | |
| **present tense singular** | The court jester **amuses** the king. |
| **present tense plural** | The court jesters **amuse** the king. |

The **past tense** tells that an action happened in the past—prior to the present time. The past tense of a regular verb is formed by adding –*d* or –*ed* to the base verb form.

EXAMPLES

| | |
|---|---|
| **past tense singular** | The black crow **swooped** across the backyard. |
| **past tense plural** | The black crows **swooped** across the backyard. |
| | |
| **past tense singular** | The court jester **amused** the king. |
| **past tense plural** | The court jesters **amused** the king. |

The **future tense** tells that an action will happen in the future. The future tense is formed by adding the word *will* or *shall* before the present verb form.

EXAMPLES

| | |
|---|---|
| **future tense singular** | The black crow **will swoop** across the backyard. |
| **future tense plural** | The black crows **will swoop** across the backyard. |
| | |
| **future tense singular** | The court jester **shall amuse** the king. |
| **future tense plural** | The court jesters **shall amuse** the king. |

## The Perfect Tenses

The **present perfect tense** expresses an action or state of being that occurred at an indefinite time in the past or an action or state of being that began in the past and continues into the present. The past perfect and future perfect tenses express an action or state of being that precedes some other point in time.

| present perfect<br>(have or has + past participle) | singular: Sam **has cooked** the Christmas goose.<br>plural: Sam and Sally **have cooked** the Christmas goose. |
|---|---|
| past perfect<br>(had + past participle) | singular: Sam **had cooked** the Christmas goose by then.<br>plural: Sam and Sally **had cooked** the Christmas goose by then. |
| future perfect<br>(will have or shall have + past participle) | singular: Sam **will have cooked** the Christmas goose by then.<br><br>plural: Sam and Sally **will have cooked** the Christmas goose by then. |

## EXERCISE 1

### Identifying Verb Tenses in Literature

Identify the tenses of the ten underlined verbs in the following literature passage. Write your answers on the corresponding lines below.

I ¹have tried often to search behind the sophistication of years for the enchantment I so easily ²found in those gifts. The essence ³escapes but its aura ⁴remains. To be allowed, no, invited, into the private lives of strangers, and to share their joys and fears, ⁵was a chance to exchange the Southern bitter wormwood for a cup of mead with Beowulf or a hot cup of tea and milk with Oliver Twist. When I ⁶said aloud, "It ⁷is a far, far better thing that I ⁸do, than I ⁹have ever done..." tears of love ¹⁰filled my eyes at my selflessness.

*from "Mrs. Flowers," page 177*
*Maya Angelou*

1. _____     6. _____

2. _____     7. _____

3. _____     8. _____

4. _____     9. _____

5. _____     10. _____

## EXERCISE 2

### Understanding Verb Tenses

Complete each of the following sentences with the form of the verb given in parentheses.

EXAMPLE
The story (present of *tell*) of Maya Angelou's experience with a mentor.
(The story *tells* of Maya Angelou's experience with a mentor.)

1. Angelou (past of *grow*) up in St. Louis, Missouri, and Stamps, Arkansas.

   _____

2. She (present of *be*) an accomplished poet, writer, and performer.

   _____

3. Students (future of *read*) Angelou's works for years to come.

   _____

4. Maya Angelou (present perfect of *received*) many awards for her poetry.

   _____

5. Much of her work (present of *deal*) with economic and racial oppression.

   _____

6. Do you think that Angelou (future perfect of *influence*) many people?

   _____

7. She wrote and (past of *produce*) many productions for theater and television.

   _____

8. Angelou (future of *go*) to Mrs. Flowers's house.

   _____

9. Mrs. Flowers (past of *be*) the most elegant and refined resident of Stamps.

   _____

10. She (past perfect of *listen*) to Mrs. Flowers's wise words very carefully.

    _____

## EXERCISE 3

### Using Verb Tenses Correctly in Your Writing

Imagine that you are an ace detective, hot on the trail of a notorious criminal who has eluded you in the past. Write a paragraph describing a sequence of events that leads finally to your capture of the criminal. Include at least one example of each of the six verb tenses: present, past, future, present perfect, past perfect, and future perfect. Use your own sheet of paper for this exercise.

**LESSON 19**

# Passive Voice and Active Voice

The **voice** of an action verb tells whether the subject of the sentence performs or receives the action. When the subject performs the action of the verb, the verb is in the **active voice**. When the subject receives the action of the verb, the verb is in the **passive voice**. The passive voice is formed from a form of *be*, used as a helping verb, and the past participle of the verb.

> EXAMPLES
> **active voice**   Nelson Mandela **gave** many speeches.
> **passive voice**   He **was awarded** the Nobel Peace Prize.
>            (The form of *be* is *was*. The past participle is *awarded*.)

Active verbs express ideas more directly. The passive voice may be used when the receiver of the action is emphasized or the performer of the action is unknown or indefinite. In this example, the persons who recognize Nelson Mandela as a leader are indefinite:

> EXAMPLE
> Nelson Mandela **is recognized** as a great leader in South Africa.

A sentence written in the passive voice can usually be revised to the active voice.

> EXAMPLES
> **passive voice**   In 1994, Nelson Mandela's autobiography **was published**.
> **active voice**   Nelson Mandela **published** his autobiography in 1994.

## EXERCISE 1

### Identifying Passive and Active Verbs

Identify the underlined verbs as either active or passive.

1. Nelson Mandela <u>dedicates</u> his life to securing freedom and justice for black people.

   _____

2. Mandela <u>was born</u> in South Africa in 1918.

   _____

3. He <u>worked</u> to end apartheid.

   _____

4. Mandela <u>spent</u> many years incarcerated.

_____

5. He <u>has received</u> over one hundred awards over four decades.

_____

6. Mandela detested racism and <u>considered</u> it a barbaric thing.

_____

7. He <u>held</u> many positions in the African National Congress.

_____

8. Mandela <u>was inaugurated</u> as the first democratically elected State President of South Africa in 1994.

_____

9. Mandela <u>retired</u> from public life in June 1999.

_____

10. His life <u>has been</u> an inspiration.

_____

## EXERCISE 2

### Understanding Passive and Active Verbs

Revise each of the following sentences so the verb is in the active voice.

EXAMPLE

**passive verb**     Short stories *are written* by many different authors.
**active verb**      Many different authors *write* short stories.

1. The slaves were guided by Harriet Tubman to safety.

_____

2. The slaves to be saved were selected by Tubman.

_____

3. The runaway slaves are being taken to Canada by her.

_____

4. As a child, Tubman was whipped and beaten by her various owners.

_____

5. If they were caught by the authorities, they would be whipped and sold South.

_____

6. The runaway slaves were given new shoes by the Quaker.

_____

7. She is denied a place to stay by a man because she has too many slaves with her.

_____

8. They were stumbling behind her due to exhaustion.

_____

9. Tubman was greeted kindly by the man at the safe house.

_____

10. They were offered lots of food by the gentleman and his wife.

_____

## EXERCISE 3

### Using Passive and Active Verbs in Your Writing

Write a synopsis for your teacher of one of your favorite stories in your literature text or in another collection. Use at least three passive verbs and three active verbs to describe what happens in the story.

_____

_____

_____

_____

_____

_____

_____

_____

**LESSON 20**

# Irregular Verbs

As you know, verb forms change to show when an action happens. The many forms of the verb are based on its three principal forms: the present, the past, and the past participle. For regular verbs, *–d* or *–ed* are added to form the past and the past participle.

EXAMPLES

| | | |
|---|---|---|
| **present** | dance | borrow |
| **past** | danced | borrowed |
| **past participle** | (has, have) danced | (has, have) borrowed |

Some regular verbs change their spelling when *–d* or *–ed* is added.

EXAMPLES

| | | |
|---|---|---|
| **present** | worry | drop |
| **past** | worried | dropped |
| **past participle** | (has, have) worried | (has, have) dropped |

Verbs that do not follow the regular pattern of adding *–d* or *–ed* are called **irregular verbs**. Some of these irregular verbs have the same spelling for their past and past participle forms. Some have the same spelling in all three principal forms. Other irregular verbs have three different forms.

EXAMPLES

| | | | |
|---|---|---|---|
| **present** | make | hit | begin |
| **past** | made | hit | began |
| **past participle** | (has, have) made | (has, have) hit | (has, have) begun |

When you're not sure whether a verb is regular or irregular, look up the verb in a dictionary. Many of the common irregular verbs are listed in the following chart.

| Pattern | Present | Past | Past Participle |
|---|---|---|---|
| **Three different forms** | begin | began | (has, have) begun |
| | drink | drank | (has, have) drunk |
| | grow | grew | (has, have) grown |
| | know | knew | (has, have) known |
| | ring | rang | (has, have) rung |
| | shrink | shrank or shrunk | (has, have) shrunk |
| | sing | sang | (has, have) sung |
| | spring | sprang or sprung | (has, have) sprung |
| | swim | swam | (has, have) swum |
| | throw | threw | (has, have) thrown |
| | write | wrote | (has, have) written |
| **Same past and past participle form** | bring | brought | (has, have) brought |
| | buy | bought | (has, have) bought |
| | catch | caught | (has, have) caught |
| | creep | crept | (has, have) crept |
| | feel | felt | (has, have) felt |
| | get | got | (has, have) got/gotten |
| | keep | kept | (has, have) kept |
| | lay | laid | (has, have) laid |
| | lead | led | (has, have) led |
| | leave | left | (has, have) left |
| | lend | lent | (has, have) lent |
| | lose | lost | (has, have) lost |
| | make | made | (has, have) made |
| | pay | paid | (has, have) paid |
| | say | said | (has, have) said |
| | seek | sought | (has, have) sought |
| | sell | sold | (has, have) sold |
| | sit | sat | (has, have) sat |
| | sleep | slept | (has, have) slept |
| | swing | swung | (has, have) swung |
| | teach | taught | (has, have) taught |
| | think | thought | (has, have) thought |
| | win | won | (has, have) won |

# EXERCISE 1

## Identifying Regular and Irregular Verbs in Literature

Identify each of the underlined verbs as either regular or irregular. Write your answers on the corresponding lines below.

We ¹elevate a few people to hero status—especially during times of armed conflict—but most of us ²know next to nothing of the battles ordinary men and women ³fought to  preserve freedom, ⁴expand democracy, and ⁵create a more just society. Many have remarked on America's historical amnesia, but its implications are hard to appreciate without recognizing how much identity [6]dissolves in the absence of memory. We [7]lose the mechanisms that grassroots social movements [8]have used successfully to shift public sentiment and [9]challenge entrenched institutional power. Equally lost are the means by which participants eventually [10]managed to prevail.

*from "Soul of a Citizen," page 197*
*Paul Rogat Loeb*

1. _____     6. _____

2. _____     7. _____

3. _____     8. _____

4. _____     9. _____

5. _____     10. _____

## EXERCISE 2

### Understanding Irregular Verbs

Write the correct past or past participle form of the irregular verb given in parentheses.

EXAMPLE
A bumblebee has (sting) their young son. (*stung*)

1. Many Americans have (try) to help a community member at some point.

   _____

2. The story (begin) with a little girl receiving a doll.

   _____

3. Unfortunately, the doctor (choose) not to help them.

   _____

4. My grandmother (sit) in her rocking chair and watched us open presents.

   _____

5. I have a cold and have not (sleep) well in days.

   _____

6. The little boy let go and the balloon (rise) into the blue sky.

   _____

7.  Marcus (pay) the clerk and took his piece of candy.

    _____

8.  She ran to the softball and (throw) it back to the pitcher.

    _____

9.  My mentor has (teach) me the important things in life.

    _____

10. The Girl Scout walked up to the first house and (ring) the doorbell.

    _____

## EXERCISE 3

### Using Irregular Verbs in Your Writing

Write a paragraph describing a dramatic life or death situation. Draw details for your paragraph from fiction, real life, or your imagination. Use at least five irregular verbs in the past and past participle forms in your paragraph.

_____

_____

_____

_____

_____

_____

_____

**LESSON 21**

# Verbals

A **verbal** is the form of a verb used as a noun, adjective, or adverb. There are three types of verbals: *gerunds, participles,* and *infinitives.*

## Participles

A **participle** is a verb form that ends in *–ing, –d,* or *–ed* and acts as an adjective, modifying a noun or a pronoun.

> EXAMPLES
> A **present participle** describes a present condition.
> The *laughing* children played in the park.
>
> A **past participle** describes something that has happened.
> The *smoked* fish was a delicious appetizer.

## Gerunds

A **gerund** is a verb form that ends in *-ing* and acts as a noun.

> EXAMPLE
> *Walking* after dark can be dangerous.

Gerunds are frequently accompanied by other associated words making up a gerund phrase ("walking after dark"). See Verbal Phrases in Lesson 40, page 214. Because gerunds and gerund phrases are nouns, they can be used in any way that a noun can be used:

| | |
|---|---|
| **as subject:** | *Being captain* of the debate team is a demanding role. |
| **as object of the verb:** | He didn't particularly like *being captain.* |
| **as object of a preposition:** | He wrote an essay about the challenges of *being captain.* |

## Infinitives

An **infinitive** consists of the base form of the verb plus the word "to," as in "to walk." Infinitives may act as adjectives, adverbs, or nouns.

> EXAMPLE
> *To try* is *to succeed.*
>
> A **present infinitive** describes a present condition.
> I like *to dream.*

The **perfect infinitive** describes a time earlier than that of the verb.
I would like *to have won* the lottery.

## EXERCISE 1

### Identifying Verbals

Circle the correct answer for the underlined part of speech in each sentence.

1. The narrator's mother kept the <u>wiggling</u> worms in a jar in the kitchen.
   a. gerund   b. participle   c. infinitive

2. The <u>cluttered</u> house was full of all sorts of random objects.
   a. gerund   b. participle   c. infinitive

3. The mother decided <u>to invite</u> future family members to the house.
   a. gerund   b. participle   c. infinitive

4. <u>Arriving</u> at dawn, Louise and her sister began to clean the house.
   a. gerund   b. participle   c. infinitive

5. They even found an old <u>milking</u> machine.
   a. gerund   b. participle   c. infinitive

6. The girls began <u>to clear</u> the house of all the junk.
   a. gerund   b. participle   c. infinitive

7. The mother did not enjoy the girls' <u>cleaning</u> escapades.
   a. gerund   b. participle   c. infinitive

8. <u>Making</u> the sweet potato soufflé and the squash casserole was Louise's job.
   a. gerund   b. participle   c. infinitive

9. The <u>dropping</u> temperature was going to bring on the first frost.
   a. gerund   b. participle   c. infinitive

10. Mr. Mitchell went <u>to look</u> at Mrs. White's garden.
    a. gerund   b. participle   c. infinitive

## EXERCISE 2

### Using Verbals in Your Writing

Write a paragraph about the chores or responsibilities you have at home. Use at least one gerund, one participle, and one infinitive in your paragraph.

_____

_____

_____

_____

**LESSON 22**

# Subject and Verb Agreement

A **singular noun** stands for *one* person, place, thing, or idea. A **plural noun** stands for *more than one* person, place, thing, or idea.

EXAMPLES

| **singular nouns** | movie | orange | daisy | goose | child |
|---|---|---|---|---|---|
| **plural nouns** | movies | oranges | daisies | geese | children |

In a sentence, a verb must be singular if its subject is singular and plural if its subject is plural. In other words, a verb must agree in number with its subject.

EXAMPLES

| **singular subject and verb** | The **orange tastes** juicy and sweet. |
|---|---|
| **plural subject and verb** | The **oranges taste** juicy and sweet. |
| **singular subject and verb** | A **daisy blooms** in the summer garden. |
| **plural subject and verb** | The **daisies bloom** in the summer garden. |
| **singular subject and verb** | A **goose wanders** near the pond. |
| **plural subject and verb** | The **geese wander** near the pond. |

Usually a verb directly follows the subject in a sentence. Sometimes, however, a prepositional phrase or a clause will separate the subject and verb. Even though the subject and verb may be separated, they must still agree in number.

EXAMPLES
The **orange** from our tree **tastes** juicy and sweet.
The **daisies**, which are bright and cheerful, **bloom** in the summer garden.

## EXERCISE 1

### Identifying Subject-Verb Agreement in Literature

Identify the underlined subjects in the passage below as either singular or plural. Then identify the subject's verb. Note how the verb agrees in number with its subject. Write your answers on the corresponding lines below.

To be sure, the [1]issues we face are complex. It's hard to comprehend the moral implications of a world in which [2]Nike pays Michael Jordan millions to appear in its ads while [3]workers at its foreign shoe factories toil away for pennies a day. The 500 richest [4]people on the planet now control more wealth than the poorest 3 billion, half the human population. Is it possible even to grasp this extraordinary imbalance? And, more important, how do we begin to redress it?

Certainly we need to decide for ourselves whether particular [5]causes are wise or foolish. But [6]we also need to believe that our individual [7]involvement is worthwhile, that what [8]we might do in the public sphere will not be in vain. The [9]challenge is as much psychological as political. As the Ethiopian proverb says, "[10]He who conceals his disease cannot be cured."

*from "Soul of a Citizen," page 197*
*Paul Rogat Loeb*

1. _____     6. _____

2. _____     7. _____

3. _____     8. _____

4. _____     9. _____

5. _____     10. _____

## EXERCISE 2

### Understanding Subject-Verb Agreement

Write the correct verb form in parentheses that agrees in number with the subject of the sentence.

1. Our city's commissioner (supports, support) the Youth Center's mural project.

   _____

2. Five members of the mural group (meets, meet) tonight to discuss the plan.

   _____

3. Luis, who is one of our talented painters, (hopes, hope) to design the mural.

   _____

4. A community project (brings, bring) people together.

   _____

5. Supplies for the mural (includes, include) paint, brushes, ladders, and scaffolding.

   _____

6. Many artists, such as Henri Matisse and Pablo Picasso, (is, are) famous for their murals.

   _____

7. A small group of citizens (opposes, oppose) the mural project.

   _____

8. Luis (argues, argue) that the mural will brighten the downtown area and attract viewers.

   _____

9. Did you know that the newspaper (has published, have published) an article about the project?

   _____

10. Two photographers from the paper (wants, want) to take pictures of the painting process.

    _____

## EXERCISE 3

### Correcting Subject-Verb Agreement

Read each of the following sentences. If the subject and verb in a sentence agree in number, write *correct*. If the subject and verb do not agree in number, correct the sentence.

1. In our state, the wetlands needs more protection.

   _____

2. A variety of animals lives in a wetland environment.

   _____

3. The wetlands in our state was hurt by land development.

   _____

4. Ducks native to our state especially thrives in this kind of environment.

   _____

5. Different factors create wetland ecosystems.

   _____

6. The work of ecologists protect many animals and plants.

   _____

7. For ecosystems, pollution cause other major problems.

   _____

8. This summer my friends is volunteers at a nearby forest preserve.

   _____

9. An ecologist study living things in the environment.

_____

10. They also learns about how to protect the environment.

_____

## EXERCISE 4

### Using Subject-Verb Agreement in Your Writing

Write a paragraph describing a community project in which you have participated
or that you would like to propose. Explain how the project benefits or would benefit
your local community. Make sure that each of your verbs agrees with its subject.

_____

_____

_____

_____

_____

_____

_____

_____

_____

_____

**LESSON 23**

# Indefinite Pronoun and Verb Agreement

In Unit 2 you learned about different types of pronouns, including indefinite pronouns. An **indefinite pronoun** does not refer to a specific person, place, or thing. Some indefinite pronouns are always singular and take singular verbs: *anybody, anyone, anything, each, either, everybody, everyone, everything, much, neither, nobody, no one, nothing, one, somebody, someone, something.*

EXAMPLES
**singular**
**No one enjoys** having a cold or the flu.
**Everything happens** at once.

Some indefinite pronouns are always plural and take plural verbs: *both, few, many, others, several.*

EXAMPLES
**plural**
**Several** of the plants **are** tropical.
**Few remember** the terrible winter of 1972.

Some indefinite pronouns can be either singular or plural, depending on their use in the sentence: *all, any, most, none, some.* They are singular when they refer to a portion or to a single person, place, or thing. They are plural when they refer to a number of individual persons, places, or things.

EXAMPLES
singular     **Some** of the driveway **needs** new cement repairs.
plural       **Some** of the guests **visit** regularly.

## EXERCISE 1

### Identifying Correct Indefinite Pronoun-Verb Agreement

Complete each sentence by identifying the correct form of the verb in parentheses.

1. Many of the weather forecasters (predicts, predict) more snow tonight.

   _____

2. Most (enlists, enlist) in the military for a minimum of two years.

   _____

3. One usually (grows, grow) after a difficult or challenging experience.

   _____

4. All of the clothes (needs, need) to be washed and ironed.

   _____

5. Everyone in town (gathers, gather) for the Fourth of July parade.

   _____

6. Nothing (prevents, prevent) me from exercising every day.

   _____

7. Most of his lawn (has, have) a lot of weeds.

   _____

8. None of the students (expects, expect) the exam to be easy.

   _____

9. Several of the paintings (hangs, hang) in the art museum.

   _____

10. Neither of the films (is, are) worth watching.

    _____

## EXERCISE 2

## Correcting Indefinite Pronoun-Verb Agreement

Write the verb form that agrees in number with the indefinite pronoun in each sentence. If a sentence contains no errors in indefinite pronoun-verb agreement, write *correct*.

1. Most of the proposal suggest additional research.

   _____

2. I hoped for a part in the play, but most of them was already taken.

   _____

3. Nobody in our family want to clean the garage this weekend.

   _____

4. Many of the dogs in the obedience competition trains for years.

   _____

5. Some of the tree branches snaps under the weight of the snow.

   _____

6. One of our old friends tell very funny stories.

   _____

7. Much happen during the first semester of school.

   _____

8. Both of the mirrors is cracked.

   _____

9. Neither Stella nor Stanley appear in the play.

   _____

10. No one understands the point of the article.

   _____

## EXERCISE 3

### Using Indefinite Pronoun-Verb Agreement in Your Writing

Write a paragraph describing your neighborhood to someone who has never seen it. Use at least five different indefinite pronouns as subjects of sentences in your paragraph. Check your paragraph to make sure that the verbs agree in number with the indefinite pronouns.

_____

_____

_____

_____

_____

_____

_____

**LESSON 24**

# Direct Objects

A **direct object** receives the action in the sentence. It usually answers the question *what?* or *whom?* To find the direct object, find the action verb in the sentence. Then ask *what?* or *whom?* about the verb.

EXAMPLES

I saw **Nicole** at the movie. (*Saw* is the action verb. Whom did I see? *Nicole* is the direct object.)

The police officer stopped **traffic**. (*Stopped* is the action verb. What did the police officer stop? *Traffic* is the direct object.)

Remember to use object pronouns for a direct object.

**singular**    me, you, him, her, it
**plural**      us, you, them

EXAMPLES
Ben asked **us** for an opinion.
Etta called **him** last night.

## EXERCISE 1

### Identifying Direct Objects

Underline each of the direct objects in each of the sentences below.

1.  The Native Americans hunted buffalo.

2.  They used them for food, shelter, and clothing.

3.  Coronado wrote a letter about how abundant the buffalo were.

4.  Herds of two million, three million, or even four million covered the earth.

5.  Even before the Native American children had teeth, they sucked buffalo meat.

6.  The Native Americans ate it all winter long.

7.  It was not surprising that they held tribal celebrations when they ate.

8.  The Indians made mittens, caps, and moccasins from the hides.

9.  The tough skin from the neck made an excellent shield.

10. The white men also valued the buffalo hides.

**LESSON 25**

# Indirect Objects

Sometimes the direct object is received by someone or something. This receiver is called the **indirect object**. It usually comes before the direct object, and it tells *to whom* the action is directed or *for whom* the action is performed. Only verbs that have direct objects can have indirect objects.

EXAMPLE
Mother bought **Jamie** a shirt. (*Bought* is the action verb. *Shirt* is the direct object because it tells what Mother bought. *Jamie* is an indirect object. It tells for whom Mother bought a shirt.)

There are two tests that you can use to identify the indirect object: (1) Look for a noun or a pronoun that precedes the direct object. (2) Determine whether the word you think is a direct object seems to be the understood object of the preposition *to* or *for*.

EXAMPLE
The librarian read the **children** a story. (The noun *story* answers the question *What did the librarian read?* so it is the direct object. The understood preposition *to* can be inserted into the sentence before the noun *children: The librarian read (to) the children a story.* Therefore, *children* is the indirect object of the sentence.)

Do not confuse direct and indirect objects with objects of prepositions. For example, the words *to* and *for* are prepositions. If the word order of the above sentence was changed to include the preposition *to*, then the sentence would read this way: *The librarian read a story to the children.* In this new sentence, the word *children* is the object of the preposition *to*; it is not the indirect object.

Remember to use object pronouns for both direct and indirect objects.

| | |
|---|---|
| **singular** | me, you, him, her, it |
| **plural** | us, you, them |

EXAMPLES
My parents bought **me** a bicycle for my birthday.
Give **them** a receipt for the tickets.

# EXERCISE 1

## Identifying Completers for Action Verbs: Direct Objects and Indirect Objects

Identify the underlined word or words in each sentence as a direct object or an indirect object.

1. The Cheyenne called the white <u>people</u> *veho.*

   _____

2. They gave <u>them</u> that <u>name</u> because, like the black widow spider, white people were very beautiful but it was dangerous to get close to them.

   _____

3. The grizzly shook its <u>head</u> and then turned and walked out of the camp.

   _____

4. Indian men wore their finest <u>clothes</u> to battle so that if they died, the enemy would know that great warriors had fallen.

   _____

5. The headdresses of eagle feathers gave <u>warriors</u> magical <u>protection</u>.

   _____

6. She made the long howling <u>cry</u> that Cheyenne women used to urge on the warriors.

   _____

7. Cheyenne women offered their <u>husbands</u> and <u>brothers</u> <u>help</u> in battle.

   _____

8. Husband and wife shared the <u>weight</u> of responsibility.

   _____

9. The Cheyenne and Lakota gave the <u>battle</u> a new <u>name</u>.

   _____

10. They honor <u>Buffalo Calf Road Woman</u> by calling the fight "Where the Girl Rescued Her Brother."

    _____

# EXERCISE 2

## Identifying Completers for Action Verbs: Direct Objects and Indirect Objects

Write the direct objects and the indirect objects that appear in the following sentences. If a sentence does not contain a direct or an indirect object, write *none.*

1. Ginelle and Peter walked quickly toward the barn.

   _____

2. The Pamers saw them at the marina.

_____

3. Jane is singing the children a collection of ballads.

_____

4. Give the gas station attendant five dollars for his help.

_____

5. The delegates met at the Waldorf Astoria Hotel in New York City.

_____

6. The institute gave many scientists and inventors new opportunities for advancement.

_____

7. Lance gave the geometry problems one more try.

_____

8. In Hawaii, gardeners can grow orchids throughout the year.

_____

9. The farmer planted seeds in rows.

_____

10. Aunt Thelma sent us a salad bowl and tongs as a wedding gift.

_____

## EXERCISE 3

### Understanding Completers for Action Verbs: Direct Objects and Indirect Objects

Supply a direct object or an indirect object to complete each of the following sentences. You may need to provide a group of words so that the sentence makes sense.

1. From the top of the building we saw _____.

2. Did you notice _____?

3. Karen told _____ the

_____.

4. She lent _____ her

_____.

5. A layer of snow covered the _____.

6. The orchestra leader gave _____ a(n)

_____ of the concert hall.

7. The editorial page of the newspaper gives _____ the

_____ to express their opinions.

8. I showed _____  _____
about the cost of buying a snowboard.

9. A group of us offered _____

_____ in completing the mural.

10. As director, Lou made many artistic and technical _____.

# EXERCISE 4

## Using Direct Objects and Indirect Objects in Your Writing

Imagine that you're a reporter for the school newspaper. Write a proposal about a program in your school that you would like to see featured on a special report on the local television station. Explain why you think the program would make an interesting or important story. Use direct and indirect objects in your proposal.

_____

_____

_____

_____

_____

_____

**LESSON 26**

# Predicate Nouns, Pronouns, and Adjectives

A **linking verb** connects a subject with a noun, pronoun, or adjective that describes it or identifies it. Linking verbs do not express action. Instead, they express a state of being and need a noun, pronoun, or adjective to complete the sentence's meaning.

In each of the following sentences, the subject and verb would not be complete without the words that follow them.

> EXAMPLES
> Isadora Duncan was a famous dancer.
> She seemed elegant and graceful.

Most linking verbs are forms of the verb *to be,* including *am, are, is, was,* and *been*. However, sometimes *to be* verbs are not linking verbs but helpers for action verbs. Other words that can be used as linking verbs include *appear, feel, grow, smell, taste, seem, sound, look, stay, feel, remain,* and *become*.

## Predicate Nouns and Predicate Pronouns

A **predicate noun** is a noun that completes a sentence that uses a linking verb, most often a form of the verb *to be*. Similarly, a **predicate pronoun** is a pronoun that completes a sentence that uses a form of the verb *to be*. In fact, the relationship between the subject and the predicate noun or pronoun is so close that the sentence usually suggests an equation. Such sentences can often be reordered without changing the meaning.

> EXAMPLES
> **predicate noun**
> Abdul was the only **boy** who attended all the meetings. (Abdul = boy)
> The only boy who attended all the meetings was Abdul. (boy = Abdul)
>
> **predicate pronoun**
> Her secret admirer could be **anyone**. (admirer = anyone)
> Anyone could be her secret admirer. (Anyone = admirer)

To find a predicate noun or pronoun, ask the same question you would ask to find a direct object.

> EXAMPLES
> My friend is a majorette. (My friend is a what? *Majorette* is the
> predicate noun that renames or identifies *friend,* the subject of the sentence.)

The lucky winner might be you. (The lucky winner might be who? *You* is the predicate pronoun that renames or identifies *winner*, the subject of the sentence.)

The person on the phone was she. (Think: She was the person on the phone.)

The chess champions were Ron and I. (Think: Ron and I were the chess champions.)

## Predicate Adjectives

A **predicate adjective** completes a sentence by modifying, or describing, the subject of a sentence. To find a predicate adjective, ask the same question you would ask to find a direct object.

EXAMPLE
Your suggestion was brilliant. (Your suggestion was what? *Brilliant* is the predicate adjective that describes *suggestion*, the subject of the sentence.)

## EXERCISE 1

### Identifying Predicate Nouns and Predicate Adjectives in Literature

Identify the underlined words in the following passages as predicate nouns or predicate adjectives. Write your answers on the corresponding lines below.

They looked a lot like ¹breccias of volcanic origin: melted rock holding together angular chunks of unmelted rock. Their presence in the drill cores did not bode well for the oil company's exploration of the area, since volcanic rock usually means that oil, even if present, is not ²easy to extract. The area from which the cores were taken did show a strange feature unlike that of a volcano—it was apparently ³part of a huge, semicircular ring with a high gravity field at the center. But because so few scientists took seriously the likelihood of a large asteroid's impact on earth, it seemed eminently ⁴sensible to assume the breccias were the ⁵products of a volcano.

*from "A Tale of Two Rocks," page 262*
*Valerie Jablow*

1. _____

2. _____

3. _____

4. _____

5. _____

# EXERCISE 2

## Identifying Predicate Nouns, Predicate Pronouns, and Predicate Adjectives

Write the predicate nouns, predicate pronouns, or predicate adjectives in each of the following sentences. If a sentence does not contain a predicate noun, predicate pronoun, or predicate adjective, write *none.*

1. *Nori,* or seaweed, is rich in vitamins and minerals.

   _____

2. It is a cure for mild irritations, such as sore throats and congestion.

   _____

3. Some doctors believe that *nori* may be useful in lowering blood pressure.

   _____

4. The seaweed *nori* is really a sea vegetable because it is purposefully cultivated.

   _____

5. It has been successful in aquaculture as well, growing on fences in underwater plantations.

   _____

6. *Nori* is salty and crisp after roasting.

   _____

7. Isahaya Bay is the source of Japan's best *nori.*

   _____

8. *Nori* becomes the wrapper for sushi, a roll made of rice, raw fish, and vegetables.

   _____

9. It also tastes delicious in soup and salads.

   _____

10. The person who first introduced me to *nori* was you.

    _____

## EXERCISE 3

### Understanding Predicate Nouns, Predicate Pronouns, and Predicate Adjectives

Complete each of the following sentences with a predicate noun, predicate pronoun, or predicate adjective. You may add a word or a group of words to help the sentence make sense. Identify your addition to the sentence as a predicate noun, predicate pronoun, or predicate adjective.

1. A good book can become a(n) _____.

   _____

2. That soup looks _____.

   _____

3. Randall's trumpet playing sounds _____.

   _____

4. The task of the builders must have been _____.

   _____

5. Are you also a(n) _____?

   _____

6. His main source of companionship is _____.

   _____

7. The computer is _____.

   _____

8. After a two-mile jog, I felt _____.

   _____

9. Samuel appears _____.

   _____

10. The best student for the position is _____.

    _____

## EXERCISE 4

### Using Predicate Nouns, Predicate Pronouns, and Predicate Adjectives in Your Writing

Choose one of your favorite types of music and write a short paragraph about it.
Highlight the music's sound, type of rhythm, instrumentation, and style. Complete
your sentences with predicate nouns, predicate pronouns, and predicate adjectives
to help your readers understand why this type of music is one of your favorites.

_____

_____

_____

_____

_____

_____

_____

_____

_____

_____

**LESSON 27**

# Adjectives and Adverbs: Choosing the Correct Modifier

Adjectives and adverbs—two kinds of **modifiers**—add meaning to nouns, adjectives, verbs, and adverbs.

An **adjective** modifies a noun or pronoun. An **adverb** is a word that modifies a verb, adjective, or other adverb.

> **EXAMPLES**
> **adjective**  Fishing is an **exciting** sport for **energetic** anglers. (*Exciting* modifies the noun *sport*; *energetic* modifies the noun *anglers.*)
> **adverb**  The fish is **too** bony for most people to eat. (*Too* modifies the adjective *bony.*)

To determine whether a modifier is an adjective or an adverb, follow these steps.

1. Look at the word that is modified.

2. Ask yourself, "Is this modified word a noun or a pronoun?" If the answer is *yes*, the modifier is an adjective. If the answer is *no*, the modifier is an adverb.

In the following example, the word *water* is modified by the word *turquoise*. The word *water* is a noun, so the word *turquoise* is an adjective.

> **EXAMPLE**
> The **turquoise water** rippled against the shore.

In the next example, the word *fit* is modified by the word *snugly*. The word *fit* is a verb; therefore, the word *snugly* is an adverb.

> **EXAMPLE**
> A snorkel mask should **fit snugly**.

## EXERCISE 1

### Identifying Adjectives and Adverbs in Literature

Identify each of the underlined words in the literature passage as either an adjective or adverb. Write your answers on the corresponding lines below.

> When the hunt was over, the women moved in with ¹sharp knives and ²pack horses. ³Swiftly they cut up the animals, and loaded them on horses. In the summer, when there were plenty of buffalo, only the ⁴best parts of the meat were kept. In the fall or winter, ⁵nearly every edible part of the animal was saved. Not counting the bones, this would amount to about ⁶five hundred

pounds of [7]freshly butchered meat—a much greater load than any [8]single horse could carry.

from "Indian Cattle," page 280
Eugene Rachlis

1. _____     5. _____

2. _____     6. _____

3. _____     7. _____

4. _____     8. _____

## EXERCISE 2

### Using Adjectives and Adverbs in Your Writing

Write a short paragraph about a famous person or someone you know who has special talents or abilities. Use adjectives and adverbs in your paragraph to describe the person's skills and how he or she uses them.

_____

_____

_____

_____

## Adjectives

**Adjectives** modify nouns by telling specific details about them.

EXAMPLES

| | |
|---|---|
| **noun** | a cat |
| **a little more specific** | an elegant cat |
| **more specific yet** | the elegant, beige cat |
| **even more specific** | a friendly, elegant, beige cat |

The articles *a, an,* and *the* are the most commonly occurring adjectives. *A* and *an* refer to any person, place, or thing in general. *The* refers to a specific person, place, or thing.

EXAMPLES

Would you like **a** cat as **a** pet? (*A* refers to an animal and a pet in general.)
**The** cat in **the** window is ours. (*The* refers to a specific cat and a specific window.)

Adjectives usually precede the words they modify, but they may also follow linking verbs.

EXAMPLES

| | |
|---|---|
| **preceding noun** | **The friendly, elegant, beige** cat greeted us at the door. |
| **following linking verb** | The cat was **slender** and **delicate**. |

Some adjectives tell *how many* or *what kind* about the nouns or pronouns they modify; nouns or pronouns tell us *who* or *what*.

> EXAMPLES
> There were **many** kittens to choose from at the shelter.
> They selected a cat with a **striped** coat.

Other adjectives tell *which one* or *which ones*.

> EXAMPLES
> **Our** cat has green eyes.
> **These** kittens are not old enough to leave their mother.

## EXERCISE 3

### Identifying Adjectives in Literature

Identify the twenty adjectives in the following passage. Tell which noun or pronoun each adjective modifies.

> I rubbed my hand through the black-spotted white fur of the ocelot, then
>
> pulled the measuring tape from my pocket. The total length of the skin was fifty
>
> inches, including the tail, which measured fifteen inches. The elongated spots
>
> almost gave the appearance of black lines in the fur. Ignacio watched me as I
>
> caressed it. He walked over, took the skin down, and handed it to me.
>
> from "Chac," page E124
> Alan Rabinowitz

## EXERCISE 4

### Understanding Adjectives

Rewrite the paragraph below, replacing general, overused adjectives with more colorful and precise choices and adding adjectives that bring the scene and the person to life.

I remember my grandmother best in her nice kitchen. She was a fine cook and baker. When I close my eyes, I can still see her stirring a pot of soup with her big spoon or getting her funny glasses fogged as she bent to take something out of the oven. She could stand for hours over her big board, her arms decorated in flour, kneading the dough for her sweet coffee cake. Grandma was good at slicing beets and taking the kernels off an ear of corn. Dad always said she was as good with a knife as a surgeon with a scalpel. Grandma never learned to read an English recipe, but she had all the wonderful dishes from Hungary preserved in her good memory.

_____

_____

_____

_____

_____

## EXERCISE 5

### Using Adjectives in Your Writing

Write a short paragraph about a person you remember. Use vivid adjectives to create a lively portrait of the person.

_____

_____

_____

_____

_____

## Adverbs

**Adverbs** modify verbs, adjectives, or other adverbs. Adverbs often tell _how, when, where,_ or _to what extent._

EXAMPLES

| | |
|---|---|
| **adverbs modify verbs** | Eagle rays glide **gracefully**. (_Gracefully_ tells how they glide.) Rays **often** lie **flat** on the bottom of the ocean. (_Often_ tells when they lie on the bottom; _flat_ tells how they lie.) |
| **adverbs modify adjectives** | These large sea creatures are **really** beautiful. (_Really_ tells to what extent they are beautiful.) The spotted eagle ray has an **almost** perfect diamond shape. (_Almost_ tells to what extent the ray's diamond shape is perfect.) |
| **adverbs modify adverbs** | The rays flap their winglike fins **very** gently. (_Very_ tells to what extent they flap their wings gently.) Eagle rays photograph **so** dramatically against a backdrop of coral. (_So_ tells how dramatically they photograph.) |

_Writing & Grammar_

## EXERCISE 6

### Identifying Adverbs in Literature

Identify the nine adverbs in the passage on the following page.

The proper technique is important in using jaguar callers, but often a cat may

come in simply out of curiosity upon hearing the sound. One man claimed to

have called in and shot a jaguar by putting a bucket over his head and grunting.

I was also to see callers made of plastic milk jugs and cardboard boxes.

Whatever was used, it was always advisable to stay up in a tree when calling,

I was told. Often, hunters said, a male jaguar will come in very angry thinking

another male is in his area.

*from "Chac," page E124*
*Alan Rabinowitz*

## EXERCISE 7

### Identifying Adverbs

Identify each adverb in the following sentences and tell whether it modifies a verb,
an adjective, or another adverb.

1. Obi-Wan constantly monitors the damaged component.

   _____

2. Jedi Knights usually carry various devices concealed in their robes.

   _____

3. Then they attack their enemies.

   _____

4. She is not particularly excited to see the movie.

   _____

5. George Lucas is perhaps best known for his work on *Star Wars*.

   _____

6. The very first visual effect was discovered completely by accident.

   _____

7. Obi-Wan is strongly influenced by Qui-Gon and other leading Jedi.

_____

8. Lightsabers rarely look exactly alike.

_____

9. Obi-Wan seriously tries to be a good student.

_____

10. The movie is really good and I hope that everyone goes to see it soon.

_____

# EXERCISE 8

## Understanding Adverbs

In most of the following sentences, an adjective form is used in place of an adverb form. Correct each such adjective. Write *correct* if the adverb in a sentence is already used correctly.

1. After several years of lessons, Janine played the banjo real well.

_____

2. The live shots of the city showed that traffic was moving very slow.

_____

3. Is it my imagination, or did the leaves change color very sudden this autumn?

_____

4. The actors in the most recent Harry Potter movie played their roles just perfect.

_____

5. Many people do not eat as well or as regularly as they should.

_____

6. Darnell copied his paper carefully, making sure that he spelled all the words correct.

_____

7. The trio performed poor from the first song to the last.

_____

8. Contact lenses cost considerable less than they used to, but glasses seem to have gotten more expensive.

_____

9. Mr. Carnelli spoke forcefully about preserving coral reefs.

_____

10. The starting time for tomorrow's game is reasonable early.

_____

# EXERCISE 9

## Using Adverbs in Your Writing

Write a short biographical sketch of your favorite novelist or short story writer. In your sketch, use adverbs to modify verbs, adjectives, and other adverbs.

_____

_____

_____

_____

_____

_____

_____

_____

_____

**LESSON 28**

# Appositives

An **appositive** is a noun that is placed next to another noun to identify it or add information about it. In these examples, the noun *Rebecca* identifies the noun *cousin,* and the noun *London* gives more information about the noun *city.* Both *Rebecca* and *London* are appositives.

> EXAMPLES
> I'd like you to meet my cousin **Rebecca**.
> My favorite city, **London**, is cold this time of year.

An **appositive phrase** is a group of words that includes an appositive and other words that modify it, such as adjectives and prepositional phrases. The group of words adds information about the noun it modifies. In the next example, the appositive phrase *a city in France* gives further information about the noun *Paris.*

> EXAMPLES
> Paris, **a city in France**, is a center of gourmet cooking and fashion.

An appositive or an appositive phrase that provides extra information about the noun is set off from the rest of the sentence with one or more commas. If, however, the appositive is needed to identify the noun, it is not set off with commas.

> EXAMPLES
> My grandfather, **a tall man with huge hands**, could build anything. (The appositive *a tall man with huge hands* gives extra information about my grandfather.)
>
> The author **Dorothy M. Johnson** wrote "Too Soon a Woman." (The appositive *Dorothy M. Johnson* identifies which author wrote "Too Soon a Woman.")

## EXERCISE 1

### Identifying Appositives

Identify the appositives and appositive phrases in the following sentences. Then write the noun or pronoun that each appositive identifies or modifies.

1. The author Dorothy M. Johnson is best known for her Western fiction.

   _____

2. Her book *Buffalo Woman* depicts life in the 1800s.

   _____

3. Mary, the runaway, refused to go back and wanted to travel with a family.

_____

4. Pa, the narrator's father, hunted for game but came up empty handed.

_____

5. His daughters, Elizabeth and Sarah, rode in the wagon.

_____

6. They find shelter, a small cabin.

_____

7. They had no food and Sarah, the narrator's sister, was complaining of hunger.

_____

8. Mary brought back food, large mushrooms, for the children to eat.

_____

9. The three of them, the narrator and his sisters, feasted on the fried mushrooms.

_____

10. Mary, the narrator's stepmother, is revealed at the end of the story.

_____

## EXERCISE 2

## Understanding Appositives

Identify the appositive or appositive phrase in each of the following sentences by underlining it. Then insert a comma or commas where they are needed to show information that is not essential to the meaning of the sentence.

1. Puerto Rico a self-governing part of the United States was settled by the explorer Juan Ponce de Léon in 1493.

2. The land that the Tainó Indians called *Borinquen* a name still used by Puerto Ricans with affection and pride was christened *San Juan* by Ponce de León.

3. Since the name of his patron saint San Juan already belonged to the island, the explorer had to choose another name for his first major settlement.

4. Optimistically, he called it *Puerto Rico* "rich port" but later switched the names of city and island.

5. Ponce de León erected a beautiful house Casa Blanca but left Puerto Rico in search of the fountain of youth before he could live in the house.

6. The islanders achieved autonomy under Spanish rule but lost it again when they became subjects ruled by a foreign power the United States as a result of the Treaty of Paris.

7. In the early 1950s, the island a one-of-a-kind commonwealth under the United States flag was again given its own constitution and government.

8. One of the most fascinating places on the island is El Yunque an exotic rain forest where ferns tower far overhead and orchids spill from tree trunks.

9. The rain forest is one of the only places where you can hear during the daytime the call of the national mascot the tiny tree frog called *coqui.*

10. The island's chief crops sugar cane, tobacco, plantains, and pineapples are shipped throughout the world.

# EXERCISE 3

## Using Appositives in Your Writing

Appositives are used frequently in travel advertising to pack as much detail as possible into a small amount of space. Write a headline that uses an appositive, such as *Visit Hollywood, Home of the Stars* or *Take a Walk by Stimson's Creek, the Original Babbling Brook.* Then write a short paragraph to convince your audience to visit the place you have chosen. Use appositives and appositive phrases to identify and provide more information about the location. Be sure to punctuate your appositives correctly.

_____

_____

_____

_____

_____

_____

_____

_____

*Writing & Grammar*

**LESSON 29**

# Positives, Comparatives, and Superlatives

The form of an adjective or adverb is often changed to show the extent or degree to which a certain quality is present.

EXAMPLES
Grace is **small** for her age. (The adjective *small* shows that the quality is present.)

Grace is **smaller** than Marie. (The quality expressed by the adjective *smaller* exists to a greater degree in one of the two people or things being compared.)

Grace is the **smallest** girl in the class. (The quality expressed by the adjective *smallest* exists to the greatest degree in one of more than two people or things being compared.)

Most modifiers have a **positive**, **comparative**, and **superlative** form of comparison. Most one-syllable modifiers and some two-syllable modifiers form their comparative and superlative degrees by adding *–er* or *–est*. Other two-syllable modifiers and most modifiers of more than two syllables use *more* and *most*.

|  | **Positives** | **Comparatives** | **Superlatives** |
|---|---|---|---|
| **Adjectives** | hungry | hungrier | hungriest |
|  | sharp | sharper | sharpest |
|  | dark | darker | darkest |
|  | daring | more daring | most daring |
| **Adverbs** | late | later | latest |
|  | soon | sooner | soonest |
|  | near | nearer | nearest |
|  | fully | more fully | most fully |

To show a decrease in the quality of a modifier, form the comparative and superlative degrees by using *less* and *least*.

EXAMPLES
eager, less eager, least eager
skeptical, less skeptical, least skeptical

Some modifiers form the comparative and superlative degrees irregularly. Check the dictionary if you are unsure about the comparison of a modifier.

EXAMPLES

| | | |
|---|---|---|
| good | better | best |
| well | better | best |
| bad | worse | worst |

## EXERCISE 1

### Identifying Positives, Comparatives, and Superlatives

Identify the underlined words in the following sentences as positive, comparative, or superlative.

1. Meriwether Lewis has been called "the <u>greatest</u> pathfinder this country has ever known."

   _____

2. William Clark, Lewis's partner, was the <u>older</u> of the two explorers.

   _____

3. Clark was also <u>more</u> experienced and <u>less</u> prone to risk taking than Lewis was.

   _____

4. President Jefferson hoped that Lewis and Clark would find the <u>most</u> direct route across the continent.

   _____

5. The Corps of Discovery experienced <u>much</u> hardship along the way as they traveled from Missouri to the Pacific Coast.

   _____

6. The teamwork and leadership of Lewis and Clark were the main reasons they are among the <u>best</u>-known explorers in history.

   _____

7. Native Americans led them through rough Rocky Mountain terrain where <u>little</u> food could be found.

   _____

8. The Corps' return trip east was not much <u>easier</u> than the trip west had been.

   _____

9. The history of Lewis and Clark is reflected <u>most</u> vividly in their journals.

_____

10. Lewis's <u>sudden</u> death on his way from the Louisiana Territory to Washington, DC seemed <u>strange</u> under the circumstances.

_____

## EXERCISE 2

### Understanding Degrees of Comparisons

For each incorrectly used adjective or adverb in the following sentences, write the correct positive, comparative, or superlative form. Write *correct* if the adjective or adverb comparison is used correctly.

1. Due to bad weather, our arrival was much latest than we had expected.

_____

_____

2. We chose the closer parking space to the mall so that Aunt Gretchen would not have far to walk.

_____

_____

3. The twins sounded cheerfuller about camp this week than they did last week.

_____

_____

4. I counted fast the number of newspapers I had received and hopped on my bike to deliver them.

_____

_____

5. Even the high mountain in Connecticut is not as taller as any of the Berkshire peaks in Massachusetts.

_____

_____

6. Which of the "Leatherstocking Tales" is best—*The Last of the Mohicans* or *The Deerslayer?*

_____

_____

7. Although not more famouser than Lewis and Clark, Zebulon Pike was also an important explorer of the American West.

_____

_____

8. The rattler's deadly venom makes it among the much feared of serpents even though its bite is not always fatal.

_____

_____

9. Will and Heather's marriage was a joyous occasion for the family.

_____

_____

10. Cheese sauce is more richer than tomato sauce.

_____

_____

# EXERCISE 3

## Using Comparisons Correctly in Your Writing

Write a review of your favorite movie, highlighting the major conflict and the way the characters resolve it. To help your readers understand what they will see, compare the movie to others of its type. Use the positive, comparative, and superlative forms of adjectives and adverbs to express your opinion about the film. Use your own sheet of paper for this exercise.

**LESSON 30**

# Contractions

**Contractions** combine two words by shortening them and joining them with an apostrophe. When you are trying to determine subjects and verbs in a sentence, write out contractions into the two words that they represent. After the contraction is written out, each word should be considered separately. Remember that a negative is never part of a verb, but is an adverb.

> EXAMPLES
> Cara **isn't** here today. (*is* = verb; *not* = adverb)
> **She'll** be back tomorrow. (*she* = subject; *will* = helping verb)
> You probably **shouldn't** call her. (*should* = helping verb; *not* = adverb)

## EXERCISE 1

### Identifying Contractions

For each of the following sentences, write the contraction and the two words it represents. Then write the verb or verb phrase.

1. Paul Bunyan's pancake griddle is so large that you can't see across it.

   _____

2. Who'll know most about Babe, the big blue ox?

   _____

3. They'd never heard that Bunyan isn't really a folklore hero.

   _____

4. Some people think that he might've begun as an advertising symbol for the Red River Lumber Company.

   _____

5. However, he's still one of our best-known national heroes.

   _____

6. If the tales of his adventures hadn't been exciting and enjoyable, they probably wouldn't have survived.

   _____

7. Lumberjacks like Paul Bunyan were called "fellers" because that's what they did: fell trees.

_____

8. It's hard to tell whether Paul Bunyan or Pecos Bill was the more accomplished worker.

_____

9. Who's the author of this version of the legend?

_____

10. What've you heard about Paul Bunyan's origins?

_____

## EXERCISE 2

### Understanding Contractions

Revise the following paragraph to make it more formal by removing all contractions.

It's clear that Americans like larger-than-life heroes. Ever since the days of the frontier, they've wanted to exploit and preserve the feats of men like Davy Crockett and Mike Fink. Whether they're nicknamed "King of the Wild Frontier" or "Snapping Turtle," these heroes express a long history of national spirit. Many of their feats can't be documented. For example, Davy Crockett probably didn't rescue the planet with bear grease when it was frozen on its axis. Events like these make legends worthwhile reading that people shouldn't avoid. Not only are the stories enjoyable, but they also convey the lore of American culture.

_____

_____

_____

_____

_____

_____

## EXERCISE 3

### Using Contractions in Your Writing

Create your own superhero. Describe her or his physical appearance and unusual abilities. Then tell about your superhero's mortal enemy. Use at least five contractions in your informal story. Use your own sheet of paper for this exercise.

**LESSON 31**

# Commonly Confused Words

The modifiers *good, well, bad,* and *badly* can be confusing because the distinctions between *good* and *well* and between *bad* and *badly* are often not followed in conversation. Confusion can also occur because *well* can function as either an adjective or an adverb.

> **EXAMPLES**
> Louis felt **bad** about losing the game. (*Bad* is an adjective. It follows the linking verb *felt* and modifies the subject *Louis.*)
>
> Ida slept **badly** the night before the test. (*Badly* is an adverb that modifies the verb *slept.*)
>
> Reggie is a **good** writer. (*Good* is an adjective that modifies the noun *writer.*)
>
> Reggie writes **well**. (*Well* is an adverb meaning "skillfully." It modifies the verb *writes.*)
>
> Reggie was sick, but today he feels **well** enough to write. (*Well* is an adjective meaning "healthy" or "in a state of satisfactory condition." It follows the linking verb *feels* and modifies the subject *he.*)

## EXERCISE 1

### Identifying Commonly Confused Words

Circle the correct form of *good, well, bad,* and *badly* in the following sentences.

1. The narrator took a nap on the couch that afternoon and slept (good, well).

2. Ignacio acted (bad, badly) and shot the tiger-cat in the tree.

3. The narrator has a (good, well) idea to pay the local people if they help him catch a cat alive.

4. Ignacio thought he did a (good, well) thing by shooting the cat.

5. The narrator tried to tell Ignacio that he did a (bad, badly) thing by killing the cat.

6. He seemed to be in a (bad, badly) mood as he stroked the skin of the cat.

7. The man played the jaguar caller really (good, well).

8. The narrator knew that with these callers things could end (bad, badly) for the jaguars.

9. It was a (good, well) trap and would be helpful with the project.

10. The jaguar was not (bad, badly) hurt; only a few scrapes on his nose.

## EXERCISE 2

## Correcting Commonly Confused Words

Correct any misuse of *good, well, bad,* and *badly* in the following sentences.
If no modifiers are misused in the sentence, write *correct*.

1. The classic 1950s car was really looking well after Guy replaced its bumpers and fenders.

   _____

2. Mr. Jablowski was embarrassed bad when he tripped over the trashcan.

   _____

3. The fish soup smelled and tasted badly.

   _____

4. After a week of antibiotics, Gillian felt well again.

   _____

5. The young golfer played good enough to get into the championship match.

   _____

6. I feel bad for the New York fans.

   _____

7. Playing good is the goal of practicing any sport.

   _____

8. Some people look well in colors like aqua and teal.

   _____

9. Suellen wasn't a bad trumpet player.

   _____

10. The whole class did well on the home economics final exam, a five-course gourmet meal.

   _____

## EXERCISE 3

## Using Commonly Confused Words Correctly in Your Writing

Write a short article for the school newspaper, about an athletic competition you recently attended, such as a basketball game or a wrestling match. Check to be sure that you have used the modifiers *good, well, bad,* and *badly* correctly.

_____

_____

_____

_____

_____

_____

_____

_____

_____

_____

_____

_____

_____

_____

_____

_____

_____

**LESSON 32**

# Prepositions and Conjunctions

Prepositions and conjunctions are the linkers of the English language. They are used to join words and phrases to the rest of a sentence. They also show the relationships between ideas. Prepositions and conjunctions help writers vary their sentences by connecting sentence parts in different ways.

A **preposition** is used to show how a noun or a pronoun is related to other words in the sentence. Some commonly used prepositions include *above, after, against, among, around, at, behind, beneath, beside, between, down, for, from, in, on, off, toward, through, to, until, upon,* and *with*.

> EXAMPLES
> The large dog tried to crawl **under** the small couch.
> She tied a purple ribbon **around** the box.

A **conjunction** is a word used to link related words, groups of words, or sentences. Like a preposition, a conjunction shows the relationship between the words it links. Some of the most commonly used conjunctions are *and, but, for, nor, or, so, yet, if, after, because, before, although, unless, while,* and *when*. Some conjunctions are used in pairs, such as *both/and, neither/nor,* and *not only/but also*.

> EXAMPLES
> We ate cereal **and** fruit for breakfast this morning.
> We were late for school **because** the alarm didn't ring.
> **Both** her sisters **and** her brothers have dark, wavy hair.

Certain words can function as either conjunctions or prepositions. There are two important differences between a word used as a preposition and one used as a conjunction.

1. A preposition always has an *object,* but a conjunction does not.

> EXAMPLES
> **preposition**    The Capatos planned to leave **before** *noon*. (The noun *noon* is the object of the preposition *before*.)
> **conjunction**    **Before** you leave, turn down the thermostat. (*Before* is not followed by an object. It introduces a group of words that depends on the rest of the sentence for meaning.)

2. A preposition introduces a prepositional phrase that connects its object with other parts of a sentence. A conjunction connects words or groups of words.

EXAMPLES
**preposition**  Adam went jogging **after** work. (*After* introduces the prepositional phrase *after work.*)

**conjunction**  Meet me **after** the game is over. (*After* connects two groups of words, *meet me* and *the game is over.*)

## EXERCISE 1

### Identifying Prepositions and Conjunctions in Literature

Identify the underlined words in the literature passage as prepositions or conjunctions. Write your answers on the corresponding lines below.

Poets make pets ¹of pretty, docile words:
I love smooth words, like gold-enameled fish
Which circle slowly ²with a silken swish,
And tender ones, like downy-feathered birds:
Words shy ³and dappled, deep-eyed deer ⁴in herds,
Come ⁵to my hand, and playful ⁶if I wish,
⁷Or purring softly at a silver dish,
Blue Persian kittens, fed ⁸on cream and curds.

*from "Pretty Words," page 346*
*Elinor Wylie*

1. _____   5. _____

2. _____   6. _____

3. _____   7. _____

4. _____   8. _____

## EXERCISE 2

### Using Prepositions and Conjunctions in Your Writing

Write a sentence for each preposition or conjunction below.

1. but (conjunction)

   _____

2. into (preposition)

   _____

3. between (preposition)

   _____

4. unless (conjunction)

_____

5. either/or (conjunction)

_____

6. for (preposition)

_____

7. for (conjunction)

_____

8. before (conjunction)

_____

9. toward (preposition)

_____

10. after (preposition)

_____

*Writing & Grammar*

**LESSON 33**

# Prepositions

A **preposition** shows the relationship that exists between the noun or pronoun that follows it and some other word or group of words in a sentence. Notice in the following sentences the number of different relationships shown between the noun *meeting* and the verb *occurred*.

EXAMPLES
The secret meeting occurred **under** the bridge.
The secret meeting occurred **near** the bridge.
The secret meeting occurred **above** the bridge.
The secret meeting occurred **behind** the bridge.
The secret meeting occurred **beside** the bridge.

The noun or pronoun that follows the preposition is called the **object of the preposition**. Together, the preposition, the object of the preposition, and the modifiers of that object form a **prepositional phrase**. In the following sentence, *to the store, for a loaf,* and *of sandwich bread* are all prepositional phrases.

I went **to** the store **for** a loaf **of** sandwich bread.

To test a word to see if it is a preposition, ask questions like "to what?" "for what?" or "of what?" The answers are "store," "loaf," and "bread." All three are objects of prepositions; therefore, there are three prepositional phrases in the sentence.

These are the most commonly used prepositions. Remember, though, that any word on this list may not always be used as a preposition. When it is used as a preposition, it will always have an object.

| Prepositions | | | |
|---|---|---|---|
| aboard | behind | for | throughout |
| about | below | from | to |
| above | beside | in | under |
| across | besides | into | underneath |
| after | between | like | until |
| against | beyond | of | up |
| along | but (meaning "except") | off | upon |
| amid | by | on | with |
| among | concerning | over | within |
| around | down | past | without |
| at | during | since | |
| before | except | through | |

# EXERCISE 1

## Identifying Prepositional Phrases in Literature

Underline the twelve prepositional phrases in the following literature passage.

In the years around the turn of the century, immigration to America reached an

all-time high. Between 1880 and 1920, 23 million immigrants arrived in the

United States. They came mainly from the countries of Europe, especially from

impoverished towns and villages in southern and eastern Europe. The only thing

they had in common was a fervent belief that in America, life would be better.

*from "Immigrant Kids," page 354*
*Russell Freedman*

# EXERCISE 2

## Understanding Prepositional Phrases

Rewrite each of the following sentences, supplying a preposition in the first
blank and an object of the preposition in the second blank. Some objects of the
preposition may be more than one word.

1. Elias dove _____ the

   _____ .

2. The orchestra practiced more _____ the

   _____ .

3. There's no use going _____ the

   _____ .

4. _____ the _____ the squirrels
   skittered.

5. We met _____ the

   _____ of _____ .

6. The students waited nervously _____ the

   _____ .

7. Tad scored a hit _____ the

   _____ .

8. Arlene was rewarded _____ her

   _____ .

9. The state was once covered _____

   _____ .

10. The letter was addressed _____

    _____ .

## EXERCISE 3

### Using Prepositional Phrases in Your Writing

Write a description of the most comfortable or comforting place you know, such as your bedroom or the front porch of a friend's house. Use prepositional phrases to locate your readers so that they can visualize the place as you walk them through it.

_____

_____

_____

_____

_____

_____

_____

_____

_____

_____

_____

_____

_____

**LESSON 34**

# Coordinating Conjunctions

A **coordinating conjunction** is a word used to join words or groups of words of equal importance in a sentence. The most common coordinating conjunctions are *and, or, nor, for, but, yet,* and *so.*

Coordinating conjunctions can connect nouns, verbs, adjectives, adverbs, prepositional phrases, and other sentence elements. Each coordinating conjunction shows a different relationship between the words that it connects.

When a coordinating conjunction joins two or more complete thoughts that could be independent sentences, then a **compound sentence** is formed. A comma is placed before the coordinating conjunction that joins the two complete thoughts.

**EXAMPLES**
Daphne is small **yet** muscular. (*Yet* shows the contrast between *small* and *muscular*. The coordinating conjunction joins two adjectives.)

The hammer is on the closet shelf **or** in the garage. (*Or* shows alternatives. The coordinating conjunction joins two prepositional phrases.)

Tina cannot fix the drainpipe, **for** the wrench is missing. (*For* shows a cause and effect relationship. The coordinating conjunction joins two complete thoughts.)

By using coordinating conjunctions to connect words and groups of words, you can express the clear relationships between ideas without needless repetition. These three sentences can be rewritten as one by using a coordinating conjunction between the nouns:

**EXAMPLES**
Lamont wanted a hamburger for lunch. Keisha also wanted a hamburger. Doug wanted one, too.

Lamont, Keisha, and Doug wanted hamburgers for lunch.

## EXERCISE 1

### Identifying Coordinating Conjunctions in Literature

Underline the four coordinating conjunctions in the literature passage below.

Men, women, and children were packed into dark, foul-smelling compartments.

They slept in narrow bunks stacked three high. They had no showers, no

lounges, and no dining rooms. Food served from huge kettles was dished into dinner pails provided by the steamship company. Because steerage conditions were crowded and uncomfortable, passengers spent as much time as possible up on deck.

The voyage was an ordeal, but it was worth it. They were on their way to America.

*from "Immigrant Kids," page 354*
*Russell Freedman*

## EXERCISE 2

### Understanding Coordinating Conjunctions

Write the coordinating conjunction that best fits the blank in each item below by linking the words, phrases, or sentences.

1. The bus _____ the train is cheaper than a taxi.

2. The science test was hard, _____ Emery knew the material.

3. Nantucket was the first whaling port in New England,

   _____ New Bedford soon became larger and more important.

4. Working on a sailboat is not easy, _____ the crew works long hours.

5. The dolphin surfaced, jumped, _____ dived in joyful freedom.

6. Mother, hoping to find a bargain _____ not expecting to find one, went to the discount store.

7. Diane's dog had a tendency to bother other animals,

   _____ she had to keep him on a leash.

8. They wanted to watch television _____ go to a movie last night.

9. Wild animals may seem friendly at times,

   _____ they cannot be trusted.

10. The dancer did not trip, _____ did she fall.

# EXERCISE 3

## Using Coordinating Conjunctions in Your Writing

Write five sentences about a possession that is meaningful to you because of what it is or because of the person who gave it to you. Use each of the seven coordinating conjunctions at least once in your sentences. Check to be sure that you use a comma and a coordinating conjunction between two complete thoughts.

_____

_____

_____

_____

_____

_____

_____

_____

_____

_____

_____

_____

_____

_____

_____

**LESSON 35**

# Interrupters

An **interrupter** is a word or phrase that breaks, or interrupts, the flow of thought in a sentence. In your writing, you will sometimes want to use an interrupter to emphasize a point.

   An interrupter is usually set off by commas or dashes from the rest of the sentence because it is not a basic part of the sentence or its meaning. The punctuation marks that set off an interrupter indicate a pause before and after the interruption.

   EXAMPLES
   They didn't expect, **however**, to find worms in the kitchen.
   Her mother, **she thought**, might be a late-blooming scientist.
   Additional experiments, **according to the mother**, were underway outside in the garden.

## EXERCISE 1

### Identifying Interrupters in Literature

Underline the four interrupters in the passage below.

   Edward Corsi, who later became United States Commissioner of Immigration,

   was a ten-year-old Italian immigrant when he sailed into New York harbor in

   1907:

      My first impressions of the New World will always remain etched in my

   memory, particularly that hazy October morning when I first saw Ellis Island.

   The steamer *Florida*, fourteen days out of Naples, filled to capacity with

   1,600 natives of Italy, had weathered one of the worst storms in our captain's

   memory; and glad we were, both children and grown-ups, to leave the open

   sea and come at last through the Narrows into the Bay.

                                                   from "Immigrant Kids," page 354
                                                   *Russell Freedman*

## EXERCISE 2

### Understanding Interrupters

Underline the interrupters in the following sentences. Then rewrite each sentence, correctly adding commas or dashes to set off each interrupter from the rest of the sentence.

1. Our science class I think will study worms next week.

   _____

2. Worms have different body shapes round or flattened that are long and flexible.

   _____

3. Nighttime of course is the best time to dig for worms in the soil.

   _____

4. Night crawlers for example are excellent worms for fishing.

   _____

5. Hooking a worm on a fishing pole according to my brother is not difficult to do.

   _____

6. After a rainstorm usually worms are plentiful on the ground.

   _____

7. Worms in addition to other insects can be beneficial to a garden.

   _____

8. They aerate the soil a very important task and enrich it with carbon dioxide.

   _____

9. Did you know that worms are invertebrates without backbones and have segmented bodies?

   _____

10. I didn't expect however that worms would be so interesting!

   _____

## EXERCISE 3

### Using Interrupters in Your Writing

Write five sentences about something you've recently studied or learned in science class. Use interrupters in the sentences. Remember to set off each interrupter with commas or dashes.

_____

_____

_____

_____

_____

_____

_____

_____

_____

_____

_____

Name: _____ Date: _____

# Interjections

An **interjection** is a part of speech that expresses feeling, such as surprise, joy, relief, urgency, pain, or anger. Common interjections include *ah, aha, alas, bravo, dear me, goodness, great, ha, help, hey, hooray, hush, indeed, mercy, of course, oh, oops, ouch, phooey, really, say, see, ugh,* and *whew.*

EXAMPLES
**Yes**, I finally finished my homework.
**Good grief**, you did what again?
**Wow**! Sam got a new car for his birthday.
**Huh**! I don't understand.

Interjections indicate different degrees of emotion. They may express intense or sudden emotion, as in *Wow! That was a surprise*. Notice that the strong expression of emotion stands alone in the sentence and is followed by an exclamation point.

Interjections can also express mild emotion, as in *Well, that was to be expected*. In this sentence, the interjection is part of the sentence and is set off only with a comma. Even when interjections are part of a sentence, they do not relate grammatically to the rest of the sentence.

## EXERCISE 1

### Identifying Interjections in Literature

Underline the interjection in the following literature excerpt.

> My sister was indeed momentarily rejected; she had been so ill and had cried so
> much that her eyes were absolutely bloodshot, and Mother was told, "Well, we can't
> let her in."
>
> *from "Immigrant Kids," page 354*
> *Russell Freedman*

## EXERCISE 2

### Understanding Interjections

For each emotion listed below, write a sentence that expresses the emotion. Include an appropriate interjection, and use either a comma or an exclamation point to set off the interjection from the sentence.

1. joy

_____

2. surprise

_____

3. anger

_____

4. delight

_____

5. fear

_____

6. extreme fatigue

_____

7. mild pain

_____

8. sorrow

_____

9. impatience

_____

10. disbelief

_____

# EXERCISE 3

## Using Interjections in Your Writing

Write a dialogue that might occur between two friends on the school bus, a parent and child on a shopping trip, or an athlete and his or her coach after a loss. Try to make your conversation realistic by using interjections to convey the emotion of the people involved. Use commas or exclamation points to punctuate your interjections correctly. Use your own sheet of paper for this exercise.

**LESSON 37**

# Nouns of Direct Address

**Nouns of direct address** say the name of the person or group spoken to. A noun of direct address is *never* the subject of the sentence.

EXAMPLES
Tamiko, will you please introduce the speaker? (*Tamiko* is the noun of direct address. *You* is the subject of the sentence.)

Tina, has Lucas finished his science project? (*Tina* is the noun of direct address. *Lucas* is the subject of the sentence.)

A noun of direct address can appear at any place in a sentence. Notice in the following examples where the nouns of direct address appear and how commas are used to set them off from the rest of the sentence.

EXAMPLES
The grass needs to be cut, Jenna, and you must start now. (*Jenna* is the noun of direct address. *Grass* and *you* are the subjects of the two independent clauses.)

Listen to the instructions, class. (*Class* is the noun of direct address. *You* is the understood subject of the sentence.)

## E X E R C I S E 1

### Identifying Nouns of Direct Address

Write the nouns of direct address that are used in the sentences below. Then write the subject of each sentence.

1. Do you know the artists, sir, who created the mural?

   _____

2. The mural project lasted ten weeks, Kristin.

   _____

3. Melinda, please explain the symbolism and imagery of the painting.

   _____

4. Class, all of you are about to become muralists.

   _____

5. The mentor artists, Cleo, provided both advice and guidance.

_____

6. Students, the Four Directions are represented by the colors red, yellow, black, and white.

_____

7. The footprint of a human being marks the first step of an ancient granite stairway, Julio.

_____

8. An important part of the project, Desiree, included writing in a journal.

_____

9. Matthew, your eagle lacks a definitive shape and specific detail.

_____

10. Because of your knowledge of eagles, Mel, you were chosen to paint the bird for the mural.

_____

## EXERCISE 2

## Understanding Nouns of Direct Address

Insert commas where needed to set off the nouns of direct address from the rest of the sentence.

1. Class does anyone have a bird feeder in his or her backyard?

_____

2. When do you notice the most birds Lee?

_____

3. With a pair of binoculars Beth you can see the birds in action without disturbing them.

_____

4. Chris there are field guides with pictures of all the species of North American birds and their scientific names.

_____

5. Birdwatchers Jake eventually learn to recognize the songs of the most common birds.

_____

6. There are books, videos, magazines, and tapes Mike to use for learning more about birds.

_____

7. Students many people join clubs to go bird watching together for fun.

_____

8. Friends it's important not to disturb nests.

_____

9. Lily it's a good idea to join a group that has already been birding locally.

_____

10. Well nature lovers there's another idea for something to do outdoors.

_____

## EXERCISE 3

### Using Nouns of Direct Address in Your Writing

Occasionally, the narrator of a story will step out of his or her role as a character in order to address the reader directly. This may happen when the narrator wants to mislead or instruct the audience. Write a paragraph in which you talk directly to your readers about something they should or should not believe about a character, behavior, or motive. You can use your favorite short story or novel, or you can write from your imagination. Be sure to punctuate nouns of direct address correctly. Use your own sheet of paper for this exercise.

**LESSON 38**

# Phrases and Clauses

Sometimes groups of words function as one part of speech. These groups of words are either *phrases* or *clauses*. Clauses have both subjects and verbs; phrases do not.

> **EXAMPLES**
> **phrase**  I need **to get another spiral notebook.**
> **phrase**  She will be elected **to the Student Council.**
> **clause**  I will watch the game **when I finish my homework.**
> **clause**  Do you know **who will be our class president?**

## EXERCISE 1

### Identifying Phrases and Clauses in Literature

Identify the underlined groups of words in the literature passage as phrases or clauses. Write your answers on the corresponding lines below.

A bat is born

Naked and blind and pale.

[1]His mother makes a pocket of her tail

And catches him. [2]He clings to her long fur

[3]By his thumbs and toes and teeth.

And then the mother dances [4]through the night

Doubling and looping, soaring, somersaulting—

[5]Her baby hangs on underneath.

*from "Bats," page 388*
*Randall Jarrell*

1. _____     4. _____

2. _____     5. _____

3. _____

# EXERCISE 2

## Using Phrases and Clauses in Your Writing

Write a complete sentence incorporating each phrase or clause below.

1. when you first open the door of a candy shop

   _____

2. about anything that is completely free

   _____

3. who the new owners are

   _____

4. that I was startled

   _____

5. after a treatment like that

   _____

6. in no time at all

   _____

7. about eight months ago

   _____

8. at the far end of the mall

   _____

9. without any people or movement

   _____

10. if only there were some easy way

   _____

**LESSON 39**

# Prepositional Phrases

## Phrases

A **phrase** is a group of words used as a single part of speech. A phrase lacks a
subject, a verb, or both; therefore, it cannot be a sentence. Common phrases include
prepositional phrases, verbal phrases, and appositive phrases.

A **prepositional phrase** consists of a preposition, its object, and any modifiers
of that object. A prepositional phrase adds information to a sentence by modifying
another word in the sentence. It may function as an adjective or an adverb.

EXAMPLES

**adjectives**   Steve wanted a videogame **with excellent graphics**. (The
prepositional phrase *with excellent graphics* tells what kind of
videogame Steve wanted. The phrase is an adjective, modifying
the noun *videogame*.) He bought the videogame at a store **on
Boston Post Road**. (The prepositional phrase *on Boston Post
Road* tells at which store Steve bought the videogame. The
phrase is an adjective, modifying the object of the prepositional
phrase *at the store*.)

**adverbs**   The deer ran **across the road**. (The prepositional phrase *across
the road* tells where the deer ran. The phrase is an adverb,
modifying the verb *ran*.) The seamstress is skillful **with a needle**.
(The prepositional phrase *with a needle* tells how the seamstress
is skillful. The phrase is an adverb, modifying the adjective
*skillful*.)

Use prepositional phrases to create sentence variety. When every sentence in a
paragraph starts with its subject, the rhythm of the sentences becomes boring.
Revise your sentences, where it is appropriate, to start some with prepositional
phrases.

EXAMPLE
Theresa threw the ball to her dogs **for fifteen minutes**.
**For fifteen minutes** Theresa threw the ball to her dogs.

## EXERCISE 1

### Identifying Prepositional Phrases in Literature

In the following literature model, write the word that each underlined group of
words modifies. Then label each prepositional phrase as an adjective or an adverb
phrase.

1. A tourist came <u>in from Orbitville</u>,

   _____

2. parked <u>in the air</u>, and said:

   _____

3. The creatures <u>of this star</u>

   _____

4. are made <u>of metal and glass</u>.

   _____

5. <u>Through the transparent parts</u>
   you can see their guts.

   _____

6. Their feet are round and roll
   <u>on diagrams</u> or long

   _____

7. measuring tapes, dark
   <u>with white lines</u>.

   _____

8. They have four eyes.
   The two <u>in the back</u> are red.

   _____

from "Southbound on the Freeway," page 380
May Swenson

## EXERCISE 2

### Understanding Prepositional Phrases

Rewrite the following sentences so that each begins with a prepositional phrase.

1. Mr. Beach left the room without a word.

   _____

2. A fat grizzly lay sleeping on the narrow ledge outside the cave.

   _____

3.  A small woodpecker with black and white feathers watched from a tree branch.

    _____

4.  The coffeemaker turns itself on at six o'clock every morning.

    _____

5.  The fog obscured the skyline across the bay.

    _____

6.  My neighbor started a greeting card business from her home office.

    _____

7.  The grocery list is underneath that stack of catalogs.

    _____

8.  Handmade pottery, rugs, and jewelry are sold at the trading post.

    _____

9.  Small groups of men played chess and checkers beneath the trees in the park.

    _____

10. A woman in jeweled glasses and a floppy hat sat at a table in the corner of the restaurant.

    _____

## EXERCISE 3

### Using Prepositional Phrases in Your Writing

Write a news story about something that happened recently in your community. Make sure your article answers the journalists' questions *Who? What? Where? When? Why?* and *How?* Use prepositional phrases in the story to help your readers visualize what happened, and try to vary the placement of the phrases in your sentences. Use your own sheet of paper for this exercise.

**LESSON 40**

# Verbal Phrases

**Verbals** are verb forms that act as namers (nouns) or modifiers (adjectives and adverbs). There are three kinds of verbals: participles, gerunds, and infinitives.

## Participial Phrases

A **participle** is a verb form that ends in *–ing, –d,* or *–ed* and acts as an adjective, modifying a noun or a pronoun. A **participial phrase** is made up of a participle and all of the words related to the participle, which may include objects, modifiers, and prepositional phrases. The entire phrase acts as an adjective.

> EXAMPLES
> **Looking intently at the photo**, Sydell was able to identify her grandmother and great-aunt. (The participle *looking,* the adverb *intently,* and the prepositional phrase *at the photo* make up the participial phrase that modifies *Sydell.*)
>
> Martha made the wreath **displayed on the front door**. (The participle *displayed* and the prepositional phrase *on the front door* make up the participial phrase that modifies *wreath.*)

For variety, begin some of your sentences with participial phrases. However, be sure to place each participial phrase close to the word it modifies. Otherwise, you may say something you do not mean.

> EXAMPLES
> **misplaced participial phrase**     I read a book about polar bears **sitting on the back porch.**
>
> **revised sentence**     **Sitting on the back porch**, I read a book about polar bears.

## EXERCISE 1

### Identifying Participial Phrases in Literature

Underline the five participial phrases in the literature passage below. Then circle the noun or pronoun that each participial phrase modifies.

> Like Lot's wife, I would trade
>
> my living blood for one last look
>
> at the house where each window held
>
> a face framed as in a family album.

And the plaza lined with palms

where my friends and I strolled in our pink

and yellow and white Sunday dresses, dreaming

of husbands, houses, and orchards where

our children would play in the leisurely summer

of our future. Gladly would I spill

my remaining years like salt upon the ground,

to gaze again on the fishermen of the bay

dragging their catch in nets glittering

like pirate gold, to the shore.

*from "Exile," page E167*
*Judith Ortiz Cofer*

## EXERCISE 2

### Understanding Participial Phrases

For each of the following participial phrases, write a complete sentence. Try to vary your sentence structure, and be sure to place the participial phrase close to the word it modifies.

1. written on pink stationery

   _____

2. celebrated on the third Monday of January

   _____

3. seen from afar

   _____

4. quoting from her favorite movie

   _____

5. sliding into home plate

   _____

6. surprised by the news

   _____

7. warning of danger

_____

8. visiting from New Orleans

_____

9. run by volunteers

_____

10. floating close to shore

_____

## EXERCISE 3

### Using Participial Phrases in Your Writing

Imagine that you want to start a business in your neighborhood. To let your
neighbors know what services you can perform for them, write a letter describing
your skills. Use participial phrases in your letter to describe what you can do and
how much you will charge for each task.

_____

_____

_____

_____

_____

_____

_____

_____

**LESSON 41**

# Appositive Phrases

An **appositive phrase** is a group of words made up of an appositive and all its modifiers. The phrase renames or identifies a noun or pronoun.

> EXAMPLES
>
> Jaime, **the Colombian foreign exchange student**, is the new wrestling champion. (The appositive phrase renames the noun *Jaime*.)
>
> The homophones ***there, their,*** and ***they're*** cause spelling problems for many people. (The appositive phrase identifies which homophones cause spelling problems.)

The first example above, *the Colombian foreign exchange student*, is a **nonessential appositive phrase**. It is not necessary to identify Jaime, who has already been named; therefore, the phrase is set off with commas. The second example, *there, their,* and *they're,* is an **essential appositive phrase**. This appositive phrase is necessary for understanding the sentence, so the phrase is not set off with commas.

Appositive phrases add variety to your writing because they can be placed at the beginning, in the middle, or at the end of a sentence. Using appositive phrases to combine sentences eliminates unimportant words and creates more fact-filled sentences. When you join two ideas with an appositive phrase, place the idea you wish to stress in the main clause and make the less important idea the appositive.

> EXAMPLES
>
> Lydia wants to become a doctor. She is the daughter of a surgeon and a pediatrician.
> Lydia, **the daughter of a surgeon and a pediatrician,** wants to become a doctor.

## EXERCISE 1

### Identifying Appositive Phrases

Write the appositive phrases you find in the sentences below. Then identify the noun or pronoun each appositive phrase describes.

1. Bats, the only mammals capable of flight, are nocturnal creatures.

   _____

2. Most bats are insectivores, animals that eat a diet of insects and small creatures.

   _____

3. Many bats retreat to caves, natural underground chambers, to hibernate.

4. *Phyllostomidae*, the leaf-nosed bats, prey on vertebrates.

5. The saying *blind as a bat* is based on a myth.

6. Bats use echolocation, the emission and reflection of sound waves, to find their food.

7. The bat, a long-furred female, carries her baby.

8. The baby bat, a pup, clings to his mother and drinks her milk.

9. There are a few species of bats in the United States that are in danger of extinction, dying out.

10. Randall Jarrell wrote "Bats," a narrative poem.

## EXERCISE 2

### Understanding Appositive Phrases

Combine each pair of sentences with an appositive or an appositive phrase.

1. Henry Wadsworth Longfellow is a great American poet. He is known for his rhyme and rhythm.

2. Poems from Europe were known as the "good" poetry. They were very popular at the time.

3. Longfellow was born in Maine. Maine is a state in the northeastern part of the country.

_____

_____

4. Longfellow was a professor at Bowdoin College. He taught French, Spanish, and Italian.

_____

_____

5. Frances Appleton was the wife of Henry Wadsworth Longfellow. She died tragically when her dress caught on fire.

_____

_____

6. "Paul Revere's Ride" is a poem about the first battle of the Revolutionary War. Longfellow wrote it.

_____

_____

7. "Paul Revere's Ride" was published on the eve of the American Civil War. It is one of Longfellow's best known and most widely read poems.

_____

_____

8. Paul Revere was a participant in the Boston Tea Party. He was a silversmith and a devoted patriot.

_____

_____

9. Longfellow wanted to create a hero, not be historically accurate. Paul Revere was the hero.

_____

_____

10. "Paul Revere's Ride" is still widely read and debated today. Historians still try to determine fact from fiction in the poem.

_____

_____

# EXERCISE 3

## Using Appositives in Your Writing

Choose a land or sea creature that you believe may be endangered. Write a short paragraph about its appearance, its behavior, and its endangered status. Use at least five appositive phrases to describe the creature in detail.

_____

_____

_____

_____

_____

_____

_____

_____

_____

_____

_____

_____

_____

_____

**LESSON 42**

# Types of Clauses within a Sentence

A **clause** is a group of words that contains a subject and verb and that functions as one part of speech. There are two types of clauses—independent and subordinate.

An **independent clause**, sometimes called a *main clause*, has a subject and a verb and expresses a complete thought. Since it can stand alone as a sentence, it is called independent.

> EXAMPLE
> Alaska is a place of thundering glaciers, towering spruces, and sparkling fjords.

A **subordinate clause** has a subject and a verb, but it doesn't express a complete thought. It can't stand alone. It must be attached to or inserted into an independent clause. That's why subordinate clauses are also called *dependent clauses*. When you combine subordinate clauses with independent clauses, you form complete sentences.

> EXAMPLES
> **Because the store was out of milk**, Ivy bought orange juice instead. (The subordinate clause *because the store was out of milk* is attached to an independent clause.)
>
> The person **who called yesterday** did not leave a message.
> (The subordinate clause *who called yesterday* is inserted into the independent clause *The person did not leave a message*.)

## EXERCISE 1

### Identifying Independent and Subordinate Clauses

Single underline the independent clauses and double underline the subordinate clauses you find in the following passage.

Like Jarrell, Roethke was both a writer and a teacher, who taught at several

colleges and universities. His writing career began in high school when a speech

of his, on the Junior Red Cross, was published all over the world in twenty-six

different languages. He published his first book of poetry, *Open House*, in 1941

and went on to publish several more volumes, including *The Waking* (1953),

which won the Pulitzer Prize.

# EXERCISE 2

## Understanding Independent and Subordinate Clauses

Label the following clauses as independent or subordinate. Then rewrite the subordinate clauses so that they are attached to or inserted into an independent clause.

1. although the man was within the first one hundred people in line

   _____

   _____

2. Barbara and Paul visited us yesterday

   _____

   _____

3. because Gwen lives in Idaho

   _____

   _____

4. whenever you decide

   _____

   _____

5. as soon as Alicia is ready to leave

   _____

   _____

6. they will

   _____

   _____

7. the cause is certain

   _____

   _____

8. which you promised to do

   _____

   _____

*Writing & Grammar*

9. unless there's no marinara sauce

_____

_____

10. call for emergency assistance

_____

_____

## Adjective Clauses

There are three types of subordinate clauses: adjective clauses, adverb clauses, and noun clauses.

An **adjective clause** is a subordinate clause that functions as an adjective. It modifies a noun or pronoun. Adjective clauses are introduced most frequently with words like the following: *that, which, who, whom, whose, when, why,* and *where.* An adjective clause follows the word it modifies.

EXAMPLES
Dale, **who is almost six feet tall**, is big for an eighth grader.
Pittsburgh is the city **where Sarah grew up**.

When an adjective clause is essential to the meaning of a sentence, it should not be set off from the rest of the sentence with commas. When an adjective clause is nonessential, it is set off with commas.

EXAMPLES

**essential**       The police officer rescued the dog **that belongs to Tommy Ellis.** Every runner **who completes the race** gets a small trophy.

**nonessential**  This dog, **which lives in the neighborhood**, is a terrier and shepherd mix. The runners, **who vary in age from six to twelve**, all go to the local elementary schools.

## EXERCISE 3

### Identifying Adjective Clauses in Literature

Write the two adjective clauses in the following excerpt.

Of the place and the hour, and the secret dread

Of the lonely belfry and the dead;

For suddenly all his thoughts are bent

On a shadowy something far away,

Where the river widens to meet the bay,—

A line of black that bends and floats

On the rising tide, like a bridge of boats.

*from "Paul Revere's Ride," page 400*
*Henry Wadsworth Longfellow*

## EXERCISE 4

## Correcting Adjective Clauses

Correct the punctuation of the adjective clauses in the following sentences. If a sentence has no punctuation errors, write *correct*.

1. Is that the man who is having the tag sale?

    _____

2. The house, that is on the hill, is over a hundred years old.

    _____

3. Bella wanted an animal companion who could walk on the beach with her.

    _____

4. The general store, which is owned by Jaime's uncle, stocks everything from needles and thread to refrigerators.

    _____

5. Evening is the time, when I enjoy climbing into the hammock to read.

    _____

6. The color that she chose for the living room is subtle but fashionable.

    _____

7. Drew whose sister is a star prefers life outside the spotlight.

    _____

8. Dimitri is someone, whom you would enjoy meeting.

    _____

9. They met in Cleveland where Suzanne was born.

    _____

10. That clock which had been in the family for three generations suddenly stopped working.

    _____

## EXERCISE 5

### Using Adjective Clauses in Your Writing

Write an autobiographical sketch of yourself for the school yearbook. Tell something about your family, your special interests, and what you especially like about school. Use at least four adjective clauses in your autobiography. Use your own sheet of paper for this exercise.

## Adverb Clauses

An **adverb clause** is a subordinate clause that functions as an adverb. It modifies a verb, an adjective, or another adverb.

> EXAMPLES
> Jim practiced basketball **any time he could**. (*Any time he could* modifies the verb *practiced*.)
> Trent is three years younger **than I am**. (*Than I am* modifies the adjective *younger*.)
> The firefighters left for work ten minutes earlier **than they usually do**. (*Than they usually do* modifies the adverb *earlier*.)

When you use an adverb clause at the beginning of a sentence, follow it with a comma. If you use an adverb clause at the end of a sentence, you generally do not need to use a comma before it.

> EXAMPLES
> If you're outdoors during a thunderstorm, don't stand under a tree.
> Don't stand under a tree if you're outdoors during a thunderstorm.

Adverb clauses often, but not always, start with a subordinating conjunction such as *after, although, because, before, if, so that, unless, when, whether,* or *while*.

## EXERCISE 6

### Identifying Adverb Clauses in Literature

Identify the two adverb clauses in the following passage.

If you dig that hole deep enough,

you'll reach China, they used to tell me,

a child in a backyard in Pennsylvania.

Not strong enough to dig that hole,

I waited twenty years,

then sailed back, half way around the world.

In Taiwan I first met Grandma.

Before she came to view, I heard

her slippered feet softly measure

the tatami floor with even step;

from "Grandma Ling," page E162
Amy Ling

## EXERCISE 7

### Understanding Adverb Clauses

Write an independent clause to attach to each of the following adverb clauses.
When you write out the complete sentences, be sure to punctuate the adverb clauses
correctly.

1. wherever the band goes

   _____

2. even though they were somewhat disorganized

   _____

3. until the teacher could show me a different approach

   _____

4. before Ida answered the question

   _____

5. than he did two years ago

   _____

6. that you were surprised by her visit

   _____

7. unless they could develop a new plan

   _____

8. when the lights went out

   _____

9. after the secretary left the office

   _____

10. so that even his grandparents laughed

   _____

## EXERCISE 8

### Using Adverb Clauses in Your Writing

A "scofflaw" is a person who disregards the law. Write a paragraph about the kind of scofflaw that disturbs you the most. Consider graffiti, jaywalking, speeding, littering, playing extremely loud stereos, or any other example of taking liberties with the legal code. In your paragraph, use at least three adverb clauses.

_____

_____

_____

_____

_____

_____

_____

_____

_____

_____

_____

_____

_____

_____

**LESSON 43**

# The Clauses of a Sentence: Simple and Compound Sentences

Sentences are classified according to the number and kind of clauses they contain. Three types of sentence structures are *simple, compound,* and *complex.*

   A **simple sentence** contains one independent clause and no subordinate clauses. It may have any number of phrases. It may also have a compound subject and a compound predicate. A simple sentence is sometimes called an independent clause because it can stand by itself.

   EXAMPLES
   The swimmers dove into the water. (simple sentence)
   *Wind and rain* lashed the tiny island. (compound subject)
   Lincoln *referred to his notes* and *then resumed speaking.* (compound predicate)

A **compound sentence** consists of two or more independent clauses that are joined together with a comma and a coordinating conjunction (*and, but, or, nor, for, yet,* or *so*) or by a semicolon.

   EXAMPLES
   Sometimes toadstools seem to appear as if by magic on a lawn after a rainy day**,** **but** of course no magic is involved.

   The Egyptian pharaohs were embalmed**, and** their mummies were hidden below the pyramids.

   It was a good fishing day at the lake**;** I caught eight large rainbow trout.

## EXERCISE 1

### Identifying Sentence Structures

Identify the numbered sentences in the passage as simple or compound. Write your answers on the corresponding lines below.

   ¹Pablo Neruda grew up in a rural area of Chile. ²Summers were hot, but winters were rainy and icy cold. ³The wet climate made for green pastures for sheep and boggy areas for rice. ⁴Sheep farmers were fortunate. ⁵They had plenty of wool for warm socks, sweaters, and hats. ⁶Neruda first wrote this poem in his native language, Spanish.

1. _____     4. _____

2. _____     5. _____

3. _____     6. _____

**LESSON 44**

# The Clauses of a Sentence: Complex Sentences

A **complex sentence** consists of one independent clause and one or more subordinate clauses. In the following examples, the independent clauses are italicized.

> EXAMPLES
> **After I returned home** and **before I did my homework**, *I helped to make dinner.*
> **As the coach always reminds the team**, *you can't be a winner without discipline.*

## EXERCISE 1

## Understanding How to Use Clauses to Create Different Sentence Structures

Expand each of the following simple sentences into a compound or complex sentence by adding a subordinate clause and/or an independent clause. Label each sentence type that you create.

1. Nora got lost.

   _____

2. The pigeons helped themselves to the crumbs.

   _____

3. The sky seems brilliant.

   _____

4. Angela's watch stopped.

   _____

5. Ben attempted a new school record.

   _____

6. Some radio programs are interesting.

   _____

7. Neither Gus nor Yvette liked ice-skating.

   _____

8. Fans made of lace or feathers were once popular with women.

_____

9. Nick read the newspaper.

_____

10. Rob doubted Lauren's claim.

_____

## EXERCISE 2

### Using Different Sentence Structures in Your Writing

A press release is an announcement of an event, a performance, or any other newsworthy item that is issued to the media. Write a press release for something happening at your school, such as a concert, art show, or play. In your press release, use a variety of simple, compound, and complex sentences.

_____

_____

_____

_____

_____

_____

_____

_____

_____

_____

_____

_____

*Writing & Grammar*

**LESSON 45**

# End Marks

An **end mark** tells the reader where a sentence ends. An end mark also shows the purpose of the sentence. The three end marks are the **period**, the **question mark**, and the **exclamation point**.

EXAMPLES

| | |
|---|---|
| **declarative sentence** | I need to stop at the library. |
| **imperative sentence** | Please sit down. |
| **interrogative sentence** | Can you help Mrs. Carlisle? |
| **exclamatory sentence** | Mrs. Carlisle needs help immediately! |

A **declarative sentence** makes a statement and ends with a period.

EXAMPLE
The carnival opens this evening.

An **imperative sentence** gives a command or makes a request. Often, the understood subject of imperative sentences is *you*.

EXAMPLE
(You) Keep your eye on the ball.

An **interrogative sentence** asks a question. It ends with a question mark.

EXAMPLE
How many objects does it take to make a collection?

An **exclamatory sentence** expresses strong feeling and ends with an exclamation point.

EXAMPLE
You must run for your life!

## E X E R C I S E  1

### Identifying Sentence Purposes in Literature

Identify each sentence in the following literature passage as declarative, interrogative, or exclamatory. Write your answers on the corresponding lines below.

WATSON. [1]Hang it, this is urgent, man!
HOLMES. [2]I will see no one before six. [3]I will not be examined. [4]I shall resist!

**WATSON.** [*Sighing.*] [5]Oh, have it your own way, then. [6]But I insist on staying with you in the meantime. [7]You need an eye keeping on you, Holmes.
**HOLMES.** Very well, Watson. [8]And now I must sleep. [9]I feel exhausted. [*Drowsily.*] [10]I wonder how a battery feels when it pours electricity into a non-conductor?

*from "The Dying Detective," page 429*
*Sir Arthur Conan Doyle*

1. _____        6. _____

2. _____        7. _____

3. _____        8. _____

4. _____        9. _____

5. _____       10. _____

## EXERCISE 2

## Understanding End Marks

Punctuate the end of each of the sentences with the correct mark of punctuation—a period, question mark, or exclamation point.

1. Have you noticed that the weather seems to be changing

2. I really love this warm weather

3. Unfortunately, these climate changes are not good for the planet

4. The levels of the oceans may be raised, and areas will be flooded

5. Doesn't the weather have an effect on food production

6. All living things depend on their environments remaining stable

7. Jack asked me if I'd heard people talk about global warming

8. Why has the earth been getting warmer

9. Scientists have determined that greenhouse gases trap energy in the atmosphere

10. We can all help by being smart about using energy

# EXERCISE 3

## Using End Marks in Your Writing

Imagine that you've been asked to lead a tour of an interesting place in your town. Write what you would say to your audience, noting facts and details that tourists would enjoy. Use sentences that end with periods, exclamation points, and question marks.

_____

_____

_____

_____

_____

_____

_____

_____

_____

_____

**LESSON 46**

# Commas

A **comma** separates words or groups of words within a sentence. Commas tell the **reader** to pause at certain spots in the sentence. These pauses help keep the reader from running together certain words and phrases when they should be kept apart. Use commas to separate items in a series. Three or more words make a series.

> **EXAMPLES**
> **Butterflies, hummingbirds, and dragonflies** darted about the garden.
> The lavish buffet included entrees of **meat, fish, fowl, and pasta.**

Use commas when you combine sentences using *and, but, or, nor, yet, so,* or *for*. Place the comma before these words.

> **EXAMPLES**
> Hunters and gatherers roamed freely**, but** farmers lived in one place.
> You can go with Ethel and her brother**, or** you can stay and help me.

Use a comma after an introductory word or phrase.

> **EXAMPLES**
> **Suddenly,** it began to rain.
> **Terrified by the thunder,** Peanut hid under the bed.

Use a comma to set off words or phrases that interrupt sentences. Use two commas if the word or phrase occurs in the middle of the sentence. Use one comma if the word or phrase comes at the beginning or at the end of a sentence.

> **EXAMPLES**
> The Great Divide is another name for the Rocky Mountains, **a range of mountains that extends from the U.S.–Mexico border to the Yukon Territory in northern California.**
>
> The Battle of Little Bighorn, **also known as "Custer's last stand,"** was a defeat for General Custer at the hands of Sioux warriors.

Use a comma to set off names used in direct address.

> **EXAMPLES**
> **Tommy,** can I read the book with you after school?
> Please insert yesterday's homework in the proper slot, **Margie.**

Use commas to separate parts of a date. Do not use a comma between the month and the year.

EXAMPLES
The Battle of Little Bighorn took place on **June 25, 1876.**
Lincoln issued the Emancipation Proclamation in **January 1863.**

Use commas to separate items in addresses. Do not use a comma between the state and the ZIP Code.

EXAMPLES
Jack London was born in **San Francisco, California.**
My grandparents are renting an apartment at **126 Ocean Boulevard, Highland Beach, Florida 33487.**

# EXERCISE 1

## Identifying Commas in Literature

Identify the use of the comma in each numbered sentence below as one of the following: series, combining sentences, or interrupter. Write your answers on the corresponding lines below.

> [1]No one will grasp what I'm talking about if I begin my letters to Kitty just out of the blue, so, albeit unwillingly, I will start by sketching in brief the story of my life.... [2]The rest of our family, however, felt the full impact of Hitler's anti-Jewish laws, so life was filled with anxiety.... [3]Jews are forbidden to visit theaters, cinemas, and other places of entertainment. Jews may not take part in public sports. [4]Swimming baths, tennis courts, hockey fields, and other sports grounds are all prohibited to them.

> *from "Anne Frank: The Diary of a Young Girl," page 488*
> *Anne Frank*

1. _____

2. _____

3. _____

4. _____

# EXERCISE 2

## Correcting Comma Use

Add commas as needed to the following sentences so that they are correctly punctuated. If a sentence is already punctuated correctly, write *correct*.

1. Anne Frank names her diary Kitty and writes in it as often as possible.

2. Anne's family moved to Amsterdam and the Germans invaded the Netherlands in 1940.

3. Miep Gies a friend of the Franks helped to hide the family.

4. On August 4 1944 the Franks were found and arrested.

5. Otto Frank Edith Frank and their two daughters go into hiding from the Nazis.

6. The Jews were required to wear a yellow star were not allowed to drive and had to attend Jewish schools.

7. Anne Frank was born in Frankfurt Germany.

8. The Franks went into hiding on July 6 1942.

9. The play *The Diary of Anne Frank* first opened at the Cort Theater, 138 West 48th Street New York NY 10036.

10. The family was taken to Auschwitz the largest of Nazi Germany's concentration camps after a three-day journey.

## EXERCISE 3

### Using Commas in Your Writing

Write a letter to a pen pal, providing background information about you and your family, your school, and your neighborhood. Choose details that will be interesting to a stranger and that will help him or her get to know you better. Be sure that you use commas correctly in your letter.

_____

_____

_____

_____

_____

_____

_____

_____

_____

**LESSON 47**

# Semicolons

A **semicolon** joins two closely related independent clauses.

> EXAMPLE
> The Bickersons hoped to attract birds; they placed birdhouses in the trees and feeders in the yard.

Conjunctions such as *and, but, so, or, nor, for,* and *yet* can be used to combine two related independent clauses. A semicolon is a punctuation mark that also joins two closely related independent clauses. The semicolon can be used in place of the comma and the conjunction. Using a semicolon instead of a comma and a coordinating conjunction adds emphasis to the second clause. The semicolon signals a pause that is longer than a comma's pause but shorter than a period's.

> EXAMPLES
> **two separate sentences**
> Stephen King is an American author. He is best known for his work in horror fiction.
>
> **joined with semicolon**
> Stephen King is an American author; he is best known for his work in horror fiction.

## EXERCISE 1

### Understanding Semicolons

Combine each pair of independent clauses by correctly placing a semicolon between them.

1. Stephen Edwin King was born in Portland, Maine, in 1947 he is the second son of Donald and Nellie Ruth Pillsbury King.

2. In college King wrote a weekly newspaper column for the school's newspaper he also was involved in student politics.

3. King married Tabitha Spruce in January of 1971 he met her in the library at the University of Maine.

4. He began by selling short stories to men's magazines many of these stories were gathered into the *Night Shift* collection.

5. King's first novel, *Carrie,* was published in 1974 it quickly became a successful novel.

6. His next novel was originally named *Second Coming* and then changed to *Jerusalem's Lot* the final title of the novel was *Salem's Lot*.

7. The King family moved to Boulder, Colorado in Colorado he wrote *The Shining*.

8. In 2003, he received the National Book Foundation Medal for Distinguished Contribution to American Letters the National Book Awards are among the most eminent literary prizes in the United States.

9. King is best known for his horror fiction novels many of his novels have been adapted for the movies.

10. In November 2008 a collection of short stories labeled *Just After Sunset* was released it featured thirteen short stories.

# EXERCISE 2

## Using Semicolons

Each independent clause that follows is the first half of a sentence. Add a semicolon and a second independent clause. Make sure that your second clause is related to the first thought and can stand alone.

1. The moon floated in the dark blue sky.

   _____

   _____

2. Gerry felt his heart pound.

   _____

   _____

3. The boat slipped quietly away from the dock.

   _____

   _____

4. Claudia's birthday was coming soon.

   _____

   _____

5. The coach will pick the captain on Tuesday.

   _____

   _____

6. The Davidsons went swimming in the ocean.

_____

_____

7. Storm warnings were issued over the radio.

_____

_____

8. Cindy worked on her project every night.

_____

_____

9. The bracelet was still missing.

_____

_____

10. Thick fog hid the house from view.

_____

_____

**LESSON 48**

# Colons

A **colon** introduces a list of items. Colons are also used between numbers that tell hours and minutes and after the greeting in a business letter.

> EXAMPLES
> The novel deals with these issues: **justice, forgiveness, and loyalty.**
> The meeting is called for **8:30** a.m.
> **Dear Accounting Department:** Please recheck your math.

## E X E R C I S E  1

### Understanding Colons

Insert colons where they are needed in the following sentences.

1. Modern theater can trace its roots back to these historical traditions prehistoric dance rituals, Native American healing ceremonies, and African storytelling.

2. There are three main types of drama Greek tragedy, comedy, and straight drama.

3. A playwright includes these in the script actors' locations on the stage, details about props, and details about sets in the script.

4. Drama and fiction share many qualities plot, characters, setting, and dialogue.

5. I began my essay on *The Diary of Anne Frank* at 800 p.m. and finished it at 1100 p.m.

6. She began her letter by saying, "Dear Mr. Rose I am interested in finding more information on famous playwrights."

7. A script includes these elements character names, setting, stage directions, and dialogue.

8. We studied a few famous playwrights William Shakespeare, Tom Stoppard, and Oscar Wilde.

9. A playwright's job is restricted by these constraints time, place, and duration.

10. At 900 a.m., I am going to the library to do more research on the different forms of drama.

## E X E R C I S E  2

### Using Colons in Your Writing

Write a letter to a travel agent asking for information on a trip you would like to make. Just for practice, try to use as many colons as you can in your letter. Use your own sheet of paper for this exercise.

**LESSON 49**

# Apostrophes

An **apostrophe** is used to form the possessive of nouns. To form the possessive of a singular noun, add an apostrophe and an s to the end of the word.

> EXAMPLES
> an hour's wait      our neighbor's car      Charles's puppy      the bus's tires

The possessive of a plural noun is formed two different ways. If the plural noun does not end in –s, you add an apostrophe and an s to the end of the word. If the plural noun ends with an s, add only an apostrophe.

> EXAMPLES
> children's hats       geese's feathers       men's conversations
> students' notebooks   five dollars' worth    servers' tips

## EXERCISE 1

## Identifying Singular and Plural Possessive Nouns

Identify each of the following possessive nouns as singular or plural.

1. Mr. Malik's factory

   _____

2. Americans' dreams of success

   _____

3. two weeks' pay

   _____

4. everybody's laughter

   _____

5. NASA's goals

   _____

6. his in-laws' home

   _____

7. her sons' rooms

   _____

8. Chris's car

   _____

9. Texas's weather

   _____

10. Keats's poetry

    _____

# EXERCISE 2

## Correcting the Use of Apostrophes

Complete each of the following sentences by inserting 's or an apostrophe alone to form the possessive case of the underlined words.

1. In the first manned flights, the <u>astronauts</u> meals were very unappetizing.

   _____

2. Anne <u>Frank</u> diary was named Kitty.

   _____

3. Sherlock <u>Holmes</u> bedroom is at 221B Baker Street.

   _____

4. The <u>houses</u> railings were in the Victorian style.

   _____

5. The cereal <u>company</u> new product became the granola bar.

   _____

6. The <u>actress</u> clothing in *The Diary of Anne Frank* was true to the time period.

   _____

7. The <u>Jews</u> bicycles were taken away.

   _____

8. <u>Anne grandmother</u> death in 1942 was very hard for her to deal with.

   _____

*Writing & Grammar*

9. It was three <u>days</u> journey to the Auschwitz concentration camp.

_____

10. The <u>playwright</u> script was a comedy.

_____

# EXERCISE 3

## Using Apostrophes in Your Writing

Write a comparison and contrast essay, showing the similarities and differences between you and your best friend. Include details about appearance, personality, interests, and other people's impressions of you and your friend. Be sure to use apostrophes correctly in your singular and plural possessive nouns.

_____

_____

_____

_____

_____

_____

_____

_____

_____

**LESSON 50**

# Quotation Marks

When you use a person's exact words in your writing, you are using a **direct quotation**. Enclose the words of a direct quotation in **quotation marks**.

EXAMPLES
"Hello," shouted Silas, "is anyone there?"
As he brought his horse to a stop, Todd invited, "Hop on, Annie, and I'll give you a ride."

A direct quotation should always begin with a capital letter. Separate a direct quotation from the rest of the sentence with a comma, question mark, or exclamation point. Do not separate the direct quotation from the rest of the sentence with a period. All punctuation marks that belong to the direct quotation itself should be placed inside the quotation marks.

EXAMPLES
"Of course I will," Mr. Hayakawa answered.
Lindsey snapped, "It's all your fault!"
"How did you get here?" Mrs. Huttlinger asked.
"Maybe," Niki pleaded, "you could teach me to dance?"

Use quotation marks to enclose the titles of short works such as short stories, poems, songs, articles, essays, and parts of books.

EXAMPLES
**short stories**                              "Born Worker," "The Tell-Tale Heart"
**poems**                                      "Grandma Ling," "The Naming of Cats"
**songs**                                      "America, the Beautiful,"
                                               "Here Comes the Sun"
**articles, essays, and parts of books**       "A Tale of Two Rocks," "Chac"

# EXERCISE 1

## Identifying the Correct Use of Quotation Marks

The following sentences include direct quotations and the titles of short works. Add the appropriate quotation marks, commas, question marks, exclamation points, and periods to the sentences.

1. Sometimes when I see land being cleared for more new buildings, I'm reminded of Joni Mitchell's famous lyric They paved paradise and put up a parking lot.

_____

_____

2. Martin Luther King Jr. said Injustice anywhere is a threat to justice everywhere.

_____

_____

3. In the song The Music of the Night the Phantom of the Opera sings Close your eyes, let your spirit start to soar, and you'll live as you've never lived before

_____

_____

4. When Amelia Earhart was the first woman passenger to fly across the Atlantic, she said I was just baggage

_____

_____

5. The migrant laborers referred to Cesar Chavez, who founded the United Farm Workers in 1965, when they said He is our Gandhi.

_____

_____

6. Heigh Ho Heigh Ho It's off to work we go sang the little men in Walt Disney's first feature-length cartoon, *Snow White and the Seven Dwarfs*

_____

_____

7. In a poem called Paul Revere's Ride, Henry Wadsworth Longfellow wrote, Listen my children, and you shall hear / Of the midnight ride of Paul Revere, / On the eighteenth of April, in Seventy-five

_____

_____

8. Though deaf and blind, Helen Keller said I seldom think about my limitations, and they never make me sad

_____

_____

9. One of my favorite images appears in Amy Lowell's poem Night Clouds, where she says The white mares of the moon are all standing on their hind legs / Pawing the green porcelain doors of the remote Heavens

_____

_____

10. On his radio program *A Prairie Home Companion,* Garrison Keillor begins his monologue by saying It has been a quiet week in Lake Wobegon

_____

_____

# EXERCISE 2

## Using Quotation Marks in Your Writing

Write a sentence in response to each direction below. Be sure to use quotation marks correctly.

1. Name your favorite song, and explain what makes it special.

_____

_____

2. Name a short story you've read, and give your thoughts about it or its author.

_____

_____

3. Tell about a poem you dislike and your reasons for disliking it.

_____

_____

4. Give a direct quotation (an actual quotation or a made-up one) at the beginning of a sentence.

_____

_____

5. Tell about a newspaper article and the reason it caught your attention.

_____

_____

**LESSON 51**

# Hyphens and Dashes

**Hyphens** are used to make a compound word or compound expression.

EXAMPLES
great-aunt Ida           one-half
CD-ROM                   short-lived
do-it-yourself           forty-two-year-old man

A **dash** is used to show a sudden break or change in thought. Note that a dash is longer in length than a hyphen. Dashes sometimes replace other marks of punctuation, such as periods, semicolons, or commas.

KATIE. *I tell you it was someone in my family and she sounded—oh, you don't understand. I knew that voice.*

*from "Sorry, Right Number," page E181*
*Stephen King*

MRS. HUDSON. Oh, I told him straightaway I was going to do that, sir. But he got so agitated—almost shouted that he wouldn't allow any doctor on the premises. You know how masterful he is, Dr. Watson.

*from "The Dying Detective," page 429*
*Sir Arthur Conan Doyle*

## EXERCISE 1

### Identifying the Correct Use of Hyphens and Dashes

Rewrite the following sentences, adding hyphens and dashes where they are appropriate.

1. Eating at least five servings of fruits and vegetables a day is healthy having more is even better for you.

   _____

2. My two year old nephew loves cherries and strawberries.

   _____

3. Dark green vegetables contain phytochemicals disease fighting nutrients.

   _____

4. Fruits and vegetables are low sodium, low calorie foods.

_____

5. They're full of antioxidants chemical compounds that may protect cells from damage.

_____

6. My great aunt puts raisins or dried cranberries on her oatmeal.

_____

7. Grab a handful of baby carrots just five or six is a serving.

_____

8. You can make a meal out of a microwave cooked sweet potato.

_____

9. Even dessert can be healthy put some sliced fruit or berries on low fat frozen yogurt.

_____

10. Snacking on berries, peaches, or other fruit yum will help keep you healthy.

_____

## EXERCISE 2

### Using Hyphens and Dashes in Your Writing

Write an informal letter to a friend about a policy at your school, such as tardiness and absences, a dress code, or a requirement of community service. Describe the policy and your reactions to it. Use hyphens and dashes in your letter. Use your own sheet of paper for this exercise.

**LESSON 52**

# Editing for Capitalization Errors

To avoid capitalization errors, check your draft for proper nouns and proper adjectives, including geographical names and directions, historical events, and titles of artworks and literary works.

Proper nouns and proper adjectives are capitalized. **A proper noun** names a specific person, place, or thing.

EXAMPLES
Brazil          Thomas Jefferson
King Arthur     Empire State Building

A **proper adjective** is either an adjective formed from a proper noun or a proper noun used as an adjective.

EXAMPLES
Brazilian coffee     Jeffersonian democracy     Arthurian legend

A possessive proper noun functions as an adjective when it modifies a noun.

EXAMPLES
Mrs. Tenor's briefcase     Italy's buildings     Jake's shoes

**Geographical names** of specific places are capitalized, including terms such as *lake, mountain, river,* or *valley* if they are used as part of a name. Do not capitalize general names for places.

EXAMPLES
| | | | |
|---|---|---|---|
| **capitalized** | Red River Valley | Adirondack Mountains | Ohio River |
| **not capitalized** | a valley | the mountains | the river |

**Geographical directions** are capitalized if they are part of a specific name of a commonly recognized region. Do not capitalize such words as *east(ern), west(ern), north(ern),* and *south(ern)* if they are used only to indicate direction.

EXAMPLES
| | | | |
|---|---|---|---|
| **capitalized** | the deep South | North Africa | East Coast |
| **not capitalized** | south of the border | the north shore | eastern Long Island |

**Historical events** are capitalized, as are special events and recognized periods of time.

EXAMPLES
Battle of Antietam     World Series
Age of Reason          Fourth of July

The **titles of artworks and literary works** are capitalized. Note that articles, conjunctions, and prepositions in the title do not need to be capitalized unless they begin the title.

EXAMPLES

*The Dying Detective*            *The Last Supper*

*The Diary of Anne Frank*        *War and Peace*

## EXERCISE 1

## Identifying Capitalized Words in Literature

For each underlined word in the following passage, identify the capitalization rule. Write your answers on the corresponding lines below.

They were ¹Jewish girls. They had come from another camp and had been walking for five days. Now we were to join them. They thought we were going to ²Oranienburg, a concentration camp like ³Auschwitz, to be gassed. Auschwitz, they said, had been captured by the ⁴Russians, who had reconquered ⁵Poland and were crossing the ⁶German frontier. The ⁷English and ⁸Americans were invading ⁹Germany from the ¹⁰West. Would a miracle happen before we reached the gas chambers?

*from "All But My Life," page 519*
*Gerda Weissmann Klein*

1. _____    6. _____

2. _____    7. _____

3. _____    8. _____

4. _____    9. _____

5. _____    10. _____

## EXERCISE 2

## Correcting Capitalization

Rewrite each sentence, correcting it for errors in capitalization.

1. Gerda Weissmann Klein has written several books including her autobiography *all but my life.*

    _____

    _____

2. Klein was born in bielitz, poland, and lived with her parents, julius and helene.

    _____

    _____

3. When Klein was fifteen, nazi germany took over poland.

_____

_____

4. The united states and great britain were invading germany.

_____

_____

5. The german soldiers forced the jews to walk up to a thousand miles in 1945.

_____

_____

6. Klein wrote many novels about her experience in the holocaust, including *the hours after.*

_____

_____

7. She has appeared on the *oprah winfrey* show and *60 minutes.*

_____

_____

8. She married kurt klein, a jewish lieutenant from America.

_____

_____

9. *One survivor remembers,* a documentary about Klein's experiences, won an academy award in 1996.

_____

_____

10. The christmas season passed, and as january of 1945 rolled around, the sirens blew almost every day.

_____

_____

## EXERCISE 3

### Using Capitalization in Your Writing

Using one of the pieces of writing that your teacher has already corrected, list the kinds of capitalization errors you make. In addition to noting proper nouns and proper adjectives, geographical names and directions, historical events, and titles of artworks and literary works, write down any problems with the pronoun *I*, the first word in a sentence, and the titles of persons. On your list, include the problem sentence, the correction, and the rule that governs the use of capitalization. You can turn your list into a checklist that you can use while editing other pieces of writing.

_____

_____

_____

_____

_____

_____

_____

_____

_____

_____

_____

_____

**LESSON 53**

# Proper Nouns and Proper Adjectives

## Proper Nouns

A **proper noun** names a specific person, place, or thing. The following kinds of proper nouns should be capitalized.

### Names of people

EXAMPLES

Martha Washington        Sandy J. Broff        Ernest Hasagawa Sr.

### Months, days, and holidays

EXAMPLES

March        Saturday        Fourth of July

### Names of religions, languages, races, and nationalities

EXAMPLES

Buddhism        Catholicism        English        Hebrew
Caucasian        African American        Canadian        Greek

Capitalize words referring to a deity: *Our Father, God, Jehovah, Yahweh, Allah.* Do not capitalize the word *god* referring to deities in ancient mythologies: *Vulcan was the god of fire.*

### Names of clubs, organizations, businesses, and institutions

EXAMPLES

Girl Scouts        Automobile Club of America
Treadway Company        Newell Hospital

### Names of awards, prizes, and medals

EXAMPLES

Academy Award        Nobel Prize        Medal of Honor

## Proper Adjectives

A **proper adjective** is either an adjective formed from a proper noun or a proper noun used as an adjective.

## Proper adjectives formed from proper nouns

EXAMPLES

Australian wombat     Shakespearean play
European settlers     Spanish ambassador

Some adjectives derived from names or nationalities are no longer capitalized because of common use: *china pattern, bowie knife, cardigan sweater, french window, russian dressing.*

## Proper nouns used as adjectives

EXAMPLES

Senate floor     Shakespeare festival     Bible class

A possessive proper noun functions as an adjective when it modifies a noun.

EXAMPLES

Mexico's coast     France's architecture     Phillip's stereo

Brand names are used as proper adjectives. Capitalize the name used as an adjective, but do not capitalize the common noun it modifies unless the word is part of the product name: *Creemie chocolates, Mr. Shell's peanuts*

## EXERCISE 1

## Identifying Proper Nouns and Proper Adjectives

Identify the proper nouns and proper adjectives in the following sentences. Single underline the proper nouns and double underline the proper adjectives.

1. Twinkies, a cream-filled sponge cake, are manufactured by Hostess.

2. Jim Irwin takes a Geiger counter with him when he explores the northeastern part of the valley.

3. To help himself calm down, Jim thinks, "My sister Ethel can't spell Nebuchadnezzar."

4. Anne Frank's family is Jewish and they are going into hiding.

5. Charley catches sight of a very small Currier & Ives locomotive with a funnel-shaped stack.

6. Sherlock Holmes's illness is just a show in the play *The Dying Detective*.

7. Margie and her brother Tommy go to school every day except Saturday and Sunday.

8. Sir Arthur Conan Doyle was born in Edinburgh, Scotland.

9. He grew up in an Irish-Catholic family and later on married Mary Foley.

10. Holmes's house is located at 221B Baker Street.

# EXERCISE 2

## Correcting Capitalization for Proper Nouns and Adjectives

Rewrite the following sentences, correcting any capitalization errors.

1. The play *The Diary of Anne Frank* won a tony award.

   _____

   _____

2. Have you ever eaten bavarian cream pie?

   _____

   _____

3. The reed language school teaches french, portuguese, and greek, among several
   other classical and modern languages.

   _____

   _____

4. The bueno airlines flight to Cancun arrived on time on friday, february 10.

   _____

   _____

5. The Raviches would like to see the refurbished winter garden theater when
   they're in new york.

   _____

   _____

6. Martin luther king jr. was assassinated in memphis, tennessee.

   _____

   _____

7. Because she was one-quarter Cherokee, Leslie was considered a native american.

   _____

   _____

8. The average person cannot comprehend einsteinian theory.

   _____

   _____

9.  Renee gave tina an african violet for her birthday.

    _____

    _____

10. Instead of joining the brownies, Kim became a member of the blackbirds, a
    service club that volunteers at daycare centers and senior citizen homes.

    _____

    _____

# EXERCISE 3

## Using Capitalization of Proper Nouns and Proper Adjectives in Your Writing

Write a product review of a new food, piece of sporting equipment, or home
appliance for a consumer magazine. Be sure to furnish specific details so that
shoppers will know what the product is, what it does, how well it does it, what it's
made of, who made it, where it can be purchased and for how much, and other
issues that will interest readers. In your review, correctly capitalize proper nouns
and proper adjectives. Use your own sheet of paper for this exercise.

**LESSON 54**

# *I* And First Words

Capitalize the pronoun *I.*

> EXAMPLE
> Last night I stayed up late to watch the Grammy Awards.

Capitalize the **first word** of each sentence.

> EXAMPLE
> We learned about the Battle of the Bulge in history class.

Capitalize the first word of a **direct quotation**. Do not capitalize the first word of a direct quotation if it continues after an interruption in the quote or the identification of the speaker. Do not capitalize an indirect quotation.

> EXAMPLES
> **direct quotation**
> "Costa Rica is a wonderful place to learn about rain and cloud forests," Mrs. Dors said wistfully to her husband.
>
> **direct quotation interrupted**
> "Orchids grow like weeds there," she explained, "and parrots roost in the trees the way purple martins line up on the telephone wires here."
>
> **indirect quotation**
> Mrs. Dors said that Costa Rica is a wonderful place to learn about rain and cloud forests.

When citing **poetry**, follow the capitalization of the original poem. Although most poets capitalize the first word of each line in a poem, as is the case in the first set of lines below, some poets do not. The second example shows how a poet uses a combination of uppercase and lowercase letters at the beginning of lines.

> Poets make pets of pretty, docile words:
> I love smooth words, like gold-enameled fish
> Which circle slowly with a silken swish,
> And tender ones, like downy-feathered birds:
> Words shy and dappled, deep-eyed deer in herds. . .
>
> *from "Pretty Words," page 346*
> *Elinor Wylie*

> If you dig that hole deep enough,
> you'll reach China, they used to tell me,
> a child in a backyard in Pennsylvania.
> Not strong enough to dig that hole,

I waited twenty years,
then sailed back, half way around the world.

*from "Grandma Ling," page EXX*
*Amy Ling*

Capitalize the first word in a **letter salutation** and the **name or title of the person** addressed.

**EXAMPLES**

Dear Aunt Sally      Dear Sir      Dear Leslie

Capitalize only the first word in **letter closings**.

**EXAMPLE**

Very truly yours      Your friend
Fondly                Warm regards

# EXERCISE 1

## Correcting Capitalization for the Pronoun *I* and First Words

Rewrite the following sentences, correcting any errors in capitalization you find. If there are no errors in the sentence, write *correct*.

1. Carmen asked, "what's going on here?"

   _____

2. Neil told her that Nothing was going on.

   _____

3. these are the sweetest peaches i've ever eaten.

   _____

4. The letter began, "to whom it may concern" and ended, "sincerely yours."

   _____

5. "night clouds," a poem by Amy lowell, begins with these two lines: "The white mares of the moon rush along the sky / Beating their golden hoofs upon the glass Heavens."

   _____

   _____

6. "dear sir" is too formal a salutation for a note to a friend.

   _____

7. "your tests came back," said the doctor, "And the news is very good."

   _____

*Writing & Grammar*

8. My cousin signs all her letters with "love, jill" and a smiley face.

_____

9. "I planted over a hundred crocuses," complained Marie. "Would you believe that only five or six flowers bloomed this spring?"

_____

_____

10. The customer service representative at the nursery said that others had complained about their crocus bulbs.

_____

_____

## EXERCISE 2

### Using Capitalization of *I* and First Words

Write a sentence for each of the directions below. Be sure to capitalize any proper nouns and proper adjectives in addition to the pronoun *I* and first words in sentences, quotations, and lines of poetry.

1. Write a sentence in which you quote a speaker or a writer. You may quote someone you know or someone famous.

_____

2. Turn the direct quotation you wrote in number 1 into an indirect quotation.

_____

3. Copy a verse from your favorite poem.

_____

4. Tell something about your grandparents and great-grandparents, including where they were born.

_____

5. Write about a religious or national holiday, such as how or when it is celebrated.

_____

**LESSON 55**

# Family Relationships and Titles of Persons

Capitalize the **titles** or **abbreviations** that come before the names of people.

> EXAMPLES
> General Bradley Collins      Dr. Stark
> Chief Justice Olivera      Ms. Lucy McGee

Capitalize a person's title when it is used as a proper noun.

> EXAMPLES
> Here is your sword, Colonel.
> We collected $500 for charity, Reverend.

Capitalize words showing **family relationships** when used as titles or as substitutes for a name.

> EXAMPLES
> Aunt Elizabeth      Grandfather      Cousin Grace

## EXERCISE 1

### Understanding Capitalization of Titles and Family Relationships

Correct the capitalization in the following items. If there are no errors, write *correct*.

1. my grandma

   _____

2. president Jefferson

   _____

3. uncle max

   _____

4. dr. hoffman

   _____

5. judge cecilia a. lefavre

   _____

6. brett winslow jr.

   _____

7. her aunt and two cousins

   _____

8. vice president buscarnera

   _____

9. a college professor

   _____

10. professor bickford

    _____

## EXERCISE 2

### Using Titles and Family Relationships in Your Writing

Write ten sentences about family members and local and national leaders. In your sentences use a variety of capitalized and lowercase titles and words for family relationships. Use your own sheet of paper for this exercise.

**LESSON 56**

# Titles of Artworks and Literary Works

Capitalize the first and last words and all important words in the titles of artworks and literary works, including titles of books, magazines, short stories, poems, songs, movies, plays, paintings, and sculpture. Do not capitalize articles (*a, an, the*), conjunctions (*and, but, for, yet*), and prepositions (*of, to, at, with*) that are less than five letters long unless they begin a title.

> **EXAMPLES**
> *Scientific American* (magazine)
> *For Whom the Bell Tolls* (book)
> "Charles" (short story)
> *Death and the Mariner* (painting)

Capitalize the titles of **religious works**.

> **EXAMPLES**
> Bible     Koran     New Testament

## EXERCISE 1

### Identifying and Correcting Errors in Capitalization of Titles of Artworks and Literary Works

Write the words that should be capitalized in the following sentences.

1. The play *the diary of anne frank* is about a Jewish family in hiding.

   _____

2. "should babies be fed milk?" was the title of one debate held between inmate teams.

   _____

3. Besides "charles," Shirley Jackson wrote the short stories "the lottery" and "the possibility of evil,"

   _____

4. Do you remember the words to Elvis Presley's "heartbreak hotel"?

   _____

5. Thomas Hart Benton's mural *the sources of country music* is on display next to Elvis's guitar in the Country Music Museum in Nashville, Tennessee.

_____

6. My neighbor read the abridged version of that novel in *reader's digest.*

_____

7. Many of the titles of Picasso's paintings are in Spanish or French, such as *"la joie de vivre,"* which translates as "the joy of life."

_____

8. In 1958 Merce Cunningham staged the ballet *arctic meet* with music by John Cage and scenery by Robert Rauschenberg.

_____

9. One of the first rock operas was *tommy* by the Who.

_____

10. *the liberator,* published by William Lloyd Garrison, was an abolitionist newspaper.

_____

## EXERCISE 2

### Using Correct Capitalization in Your Writing

Imagine that an eighth-grade class from a school in Belgium wants to know more about American teenagers and how they spend their leisure time. Make a list of book, movie, television show, magazine, short story, album, song, poem, and painting titles that present a realistic portrait of people your age. Beside each reference, write a short summary of its theme or message. Be sure to capitalize your references correctly. Use your own sheet of paper for this exercise.

LESSON 57

# Incorrect Subject-Verb Agreement

A subject and its verb must agree in number. Use singular verb forms with singular subjects and plural verb forms with plural subjects.

## Intervening Words

A prepositional phrase that comes between a subject and a verb usually does not determine whether the subject is singular or plural.

> EXAMPLES
> The **guard** at the tower **protects** the castle. (*guard protects*—singular)
> The **librarian**, along with two aides, **hopes** to attend the meeting. (*librarian hopes*—singular)
> The **students** in this school **act** friendly. (*students act*—plural)
> The **chapters** at the beginning of the book **are** the most exciting. (*chapters are*—plural)

In some cases the *object* of the preposition determines the number of the verb.

> EXAMPLES
> None of the **cake** was eaten.
> None of the **cakes** were eaten.

## Compound Subjects

Use a plural verb with most compound subjects connected by *and.*

> EXAMPLES
> <u>Harriet and her sister</u> **talk** on the phone every night.
> <u>Squirrels, chipmunks, and moles</u> **dig** holes in the garden.

Use a singular verb with a compound subject that refers to one person or thing or that generally conveys the idea of a unit.

> EXAMPLES
> Peanut butter and jelly on a banana is a tasty snack. (one dish)
> Wear and tear often **results** from long use. (one condition)

Use a singular verb with a compound subject made up of singular nouns or pronouns connected by *or* or *nor.* Use a plural verb with a compound subject formed from plural nouns or pronouns.

**singular**
Neither Ellie nor Charlotte **plays** basketball.
Either the sheepdog or the afghan **requires** much grooming.

**plural**
Either shoes or boots **are** on sale this week.
Neither the children nor their friends **watch** television.

When a compound subject consists of a singular subject and a plural subject connected by *or* or *nor*, use a verb that agrees in number with the subject that is closer to it in the sentence.

EXAMPLES
Either Dan or his parents **lead** the meeting this evening. (*parents lead*—plural)
Neither the students nor the teacher **eats** in the classroom. (*teacher eats*—singular)

## Indefinite Pronouns as Subjects

**Indefinite pronouns** are pronouns that refer to people or things in general. Some indefinite pronouns are always singular and take singular verbs: *anybody, anyone, anything, each, either, everybody, everyone, everything, much, neither, nobody, no one, nothing, one, other, somebody, someone, something.*

EXAMPLES
**No one** catches fish in February. (*no one catches*—singular)
**Everyone** likes a good story. (*everyone likes*—singular)

Some indefinite pronouns are always plural and take plural verbs: *several, both, few, many.*

EXAMPLES
**Many** are called, but **few** are chosen. (*many are, few are*—plural)
**Both** were lost at sea. (*both were*—plural)

Some indefinite pronouns can be either singular or plural, depending on their use in the sentence: *all, any, enough, more, most, none, plenty, some.* They are singular when they refer to a portion or to a single person, place, or thing. They are plural when they refer to a number of individual persons, places, or things. In some cases, the object of the preposition determines whether the verb is singular or plural.

EXAMPLES
**Most** of our vacation was enjoyable. (*Most* refers to a portion of the weekend and is therefore singular.)
**Most** of the cookies taste delicious. (*Most* refers to multiple cookies and is therefore plural.)

## Inverted Word Order

In questions and in sentences beginning with *Here or There,* the verb appears before the subject. In these sentences with inverted word order, you must identify the subject and then make the verb agree with it in number. Saying the sentence to yourself in normal order often helps.

**EXAMPLES**

Under the bed **were** six of the dog's toys. (*toys were*—plural)

Here **is** my plan for the weekend. (*plan is*—singular)

Where **are** the directions to Lara's house? (*directions are*—plural)

There **are** two restaurants and a pet store on South Street. (*restaurants and store are*—plural)

# EXERCISE 1

## Identifying Problems with Subject-Verb Agreement

Underline the correct verb form in parentheses that agrees in number with the subject of the sentence.

1. The Pacific Ocean (freezes, freeze), and Paul Bunyan hauls snow over from China.

2. The men (dances, dance), and the sparks from their boots (lights, light) up the area.

3. Benny, the Little Blue Ox, (grows, grow) two feet every time Paul Bunyan (looks, look) at him.

4. The two mosquitoes happily (eats, eat) one of Paul Bunyan's oxen.

5. The stories of Paul Bunyan (is, are) still told today.

6. Four men, with a hog fastened to each snowshoe, (skates, skate) on the griddle while the cook (flips, flip) pancakes.

7. Many towns in the Midwest (claims, claim) to be the birthplace of Paul Bunyan.

8. Carl Sandburg, an accomplished poet and writer, (was, were) born in Galesburg, Illinois.

9. Both Robert Frost and Carl Sandburg (was, were) known as people's poets.

10. A tall tale (has, have) exaggerated details and a larger-than-life hero.

# EXERCISE 2

## Correcting Subject-Verb Agreement Problems

Rewrite the verb form so that it agrees in number with the subject of each sentence. If there are no subject-verb agreement problems in the sentence, write *correct*.

1. The glass next to the cups look clean.

   _____

2. My aunt, along with three of her friends, have left for Egypt.

   _____

3. The summary, plus all your notes, has to be turned in tomorrow.

   _____

*Writing & Grammar*

4.  The radio towers on the highest hill north of the city transmits signals along the shoreline.

    _____

5.  I wanted to borrow a biography, but most of them was already checked out.

    _____

6.  Delilah, Amos, and my sister Rachel thinks that the Ninjas will win the state championship.

    _____

7.  Nobody in our class want to be the master of ceremonies for the talent show.

    _____

8.  Neither Elisa nor her parents like musical comedies.

    _____

9.  There go either Ted or Paul.

    _____

10. Beneath the photographs on the refrigerator door was a list of names and addresses.

    _____

## EXERCISE 3

### Using Correct Subject-Verb Agreement in Your Writing

Some of the following subjects and verbs are singular, and some are plural. Write a sentence using each of the following three word groups. Then change each subject and verb from singular to plural or from plural to singular and write three new sentences.

1.  birthday present was

    _____

2.  dog howls

    _____

3.  children laugh and play

    _____

**LESSON 58**

# Avoiding Double Negatives

Make sure that you use only one of the following negatives in each clause: *not, nobody, none, nothing, hardly, can't, doesn't, won't, isn't, aren't*. A **double negative** is the use of two negative words together when only one is needed. Correct double negatives by removing one of the negative words or by replacing one of the negative words with a positive word.

EXAMPLES
**double negative**      I can't hardly hear you.
**corrected sentence**   I can hardly hear you.
                         I can't hear you.

**double negative**      Delores isn't never around after school.
**corrected sentence**   Delores isn't ever around after school.
                         Delores isn't around after school.

## EXERCISE 1

### Identifying Double Negatives

Underline the correct word in parentheses to complete each sentence. After you have completed the exercise, read each sentence aloud with the correct word in place.

1. Holly and Max didn't take (no, any) jackets with them to the outdoor concert.

2. It (was, wasn't) hardly cold when they left the house in the early evening.

3. They haven't (never, ever) misjudged the weather so badly as they did that night.

4. They had never experienced (nothing, anything) like the bone-chilling cold once the sun went down.

5. They (couldn't, could) barely concentrate on the music because they were so cold.

6. They (were, weren't) hardly able to enjoy the orchestra.

7. It's unfortunate that (someone, no one) couldn't have warned them about the weather.

8. Didn't they (ever, never) check the weather forecast?

9. There was hardly (nowhere, anywhere) for them to get warm.

10. The snack bar didn't even have (any, no) hot chocolate.

# EXERCISE 2

## Correcting Double Negatives

Rewrite the following sentences to remove the double negative. Remember that you can either remove one of the negative words or replace it with a positive word. If a sentence does not contain a double negative, write *correct*. After you have corrected the sentences, read each one aloud to train your ear to hear the correct usage.

1. Marcy doesn't have no clean t-shirts.

   _____

2. I can't find nothing wrong in this picture.

   _____

3. Ed's throat is so sore that he can't hardly speak above a whisper.

   _____

4. Mrs. Neiman couldn't scarcely hear him.

   _____

5. We didn't see nobody in the gym.

   _____

6. Sam and Dave didn't do no work on the group project.

   _____

7. They didn't never see such a spectacle as the Fourth of July fireworks.

   _____

8. We haven't no bananas or oranges left.

   _____

9. Sheldon doesn't make hardly no money.

   _____

10. The girls complained that they never saw nothing of interest at the mall.

    _____

# EXERCISE 3

## Using Negatives Correctly in Your Writing

Write a sentence using each of the following negative words. Avoid using any double negatives in your sentences.

1. no one

_____

2. never

_____

3. no

_____

4. nobody

_____

5. not

_____

6. nothing

_____

7. nowhere

_____

8. barely

_____

9. hardly

_____

10. scarcely

_____

**LESSON 59**

# Avoiding Dangling Modifiers

Place modifying phrases and clauses as close as possible to the words they modify; otherwise, your sentences may be unclear or unintentionally humorous.

A **dangling modifier** has nothing to modify because the word it would logically modify is not present in the sentence. In the following sentence, the modifying phrase has no logical object. The sentence says that the deer and raccoons were driving.

EXAMPLE
Driving through the park, deer and raccoons were seen.

You can eliminate dangling modifiers by rewriting the sentence so that an appropriate word is provided for the modifier to modify. You can also expand a dangling phrase into a full subordinate clause.

EXAMPLES
Driving through the park, we saw deer and raccoons.
As we were driving through the park, we saw deer and raccoons.

## EXERCISE 1

## Correcting Dangling Modifiers

Rewrite each sentence to correct the dangling modifier.

1. Having written the essay, the TV was turned on.

   _____

   _____

2. While driving down the highway, a bad car accident was seen.

   _____

   _____

3. Sailing up the river, a bald eagle was seen.

   _____

   _____

4.  Sitting in my car, the neighbor ran through the sprinkler.

_____

_____

5.  Finishing the steak and potatoes, the plate was licked clean by the dog.

_____

_____

6.  Looking out the window, the flowers were in bloom.

_____

_____

7.  While reading the book, the phone rang.

_____

_____

8.  While shopping at the store, the jar fell off the shelf.

_____

_____

9.  Kicking the ball, the goal was open.

_____

_____

10. Crunching on a granola bar, the bear walked through the woods.

_____

_____

**LESSON 60**

# Avoiding Misplaced Modifiers

A **misplaced modifier** is located too far from the word it should modify.

> EXAMPLE
> We returned to Pittsburgh after a week's vacation on Sunday.

You can revise a misplaced modifier by moving it closer to the word it modifies.

> EXAMPLES
> We returned to Pittsburgh on Sunday after a week's vacation.
> On Sunday we returned to Pittsburgh after a week's vacation.

## EXERCISE 1

### Identifying Dangling and Misplaced Modifiers

Underline the dangling or misplaced modifiers. Identify the dangling modifiers in the following sentences by writing *DM*. Identify the misplaced modifiers by writing *MM*.

_____  1. A huge tree branch fell as we rounded the corner with a crash.

_____  2. The beautiful new crystal bowl is sitting in the center of the dining room table filled with fruit.

_____  3. Coming home late, the house was dark.

_____  4. The little girl had a red ribbon in her hair that was tied in a bow.

_____  5. Before setting off on the hike, our water supply was replenished.

_____  6. The children approached the old house by a winding path, which was said to be haunted.

_____  7. To take good pictures, a good camera must be used.

_____  8. To cook a perfect quiche, the eggs must be very fresh.

_____  9. After putting a worm on my hook, the fish began to bite.

_____  10. John borrowed a stereo system from a friend with excellent speakers.

# EXERCISE 2

## Correcting Dangling and Misplaced Modifiers

Revise the sentences in Exercise 1 so that the modifiers are placed as close as possible to the words they modify.

1. _____

2. _____

3. _____

4. _____

5. _____

6. _____

7. _____

8. _____

9. _____

10. _____

# EXERCISE 3

## Using Modifiers Correctly in Your Writing

Expand each of the following sentences by adding a phrase or clause that provides detail. Be sure to place your phrases and clauses as close as possible to the words they modify.

1. Glen refused any attempt to help.

   _____

   _____

2. The bloodhounds pursued their quarry.

   _____

   _____

3. The entire boardwalk was smashed to bits.

   _____

   _____

4. Sweat ran down the faces of the people.

_____

_____

5. It's wise to be as brief as possible.

_____

_____

6. Every note should sound crisp and sharp.

_____

_____

7. The senator departed from her prepared remarks.

_____

_____

8. The manuscript was hard to read.

_____

_____

9. The firefighters entered the burning building to save the dog and her newborn litter.

_____

_____

10. I found myself involved in an unpleasant disagreement with a sales clerk.

_____

_____

**LESSON 61**

# Maintaining Consistent Verb Tense

Verb tense indicates *when* (past, present, future) the action of the verb occurs. Changes in verb tense help readers understand the relationships among various events. However, unnecessary or inconsistent shifts in tense can cause confusion. Writing should not shift from one tense to another if the time frame for each action or state is the same. Avoid shifting verb tenses in your writing, unless you want to show that actions occur at different times.

EXAMPLES

**inconsistent**    The path climbed up from the creek bed, and the foliage changes dramatically. (The past tense verb *climbed* is not consistent with the present tense verb *changes*.)

**consistent**    The path climbed up from the creek bed, and the foliage changed dramatically. (Both verbs—*climbed* and *changed*—are in the past tense.)

## EXERCISE 1

### Correcting Inconsistent Verb Tense

Rewrite each sentence to correct the verb tense changes.

1. Tall tales are a fundamental part of American folklore and were thought to come from stories from the men of the western frontier.

   _____

   _____

2. When Pecos Bill was a baby, his mother give him milk from a mountain lion.

   _____

   _____

3. Bill had over a dozen brothers and sisters, but they are ordinary children.

   _____

   _____

4. Bill falls out of the wagon and was left behind by his family.

   _____

   _____

5. He meets a pack of coyotes and lived with them.

_____

_____

6. Since he didn't see any humans during that time, he thinks he is a coyote himself.

_____

_____

7. A cowboy finds Bill and taught him how to speak like a human.

_____

_____

8. Bill stretches out a snake and used it for a lasso.

_____

_____

9. Pecos Bill was one of the best cowboys in the Old West, and he invents many useful tools.

_____

_____

10. Pecos Bill and Slue-Foot Sue raised a big family, and the children grow up to be cowboys and cowgirls.

_____

_____

## EXERCISE 2

### Using Consistent Verb Tense

Write a short paragraph about a concert or event you have attended in the past or about a concert or event you would like to attend in the future. Make sure that you use consistent verb tenses throughout your paragraph.

_____

_____

_____

_____

**LESSON 62**

# Sentence Fragments

A sentence contains a subject and a verb and expresses a complete thought. A **sentence fragment** is a word group that does not express a complete thought but that has been punctuated as though it does.

EXAMPLES

| | |
|---|---|
| **complete sentence** | The pale moon rose over the mountains. |
| **sentence fragment** | Rose over the mountains. (The subject is missing.) |
| **sentence fragment** | The pale moon. (The verb is missing.) |
| **sentence fragment** | Over the mountains. (The subject and verb are missing.) |

As a rule, sentence fragments should be avoided. For style reasons, however, authors sometimes include sentence fragments in their work.

## EXERCISE 1

### Identifying Sentence Fragments in Literature

Identify each of the following items as either a sentence or a sentence fragment.

1. Had to.                                   _____

2. Call her Sarah.                           _____

3. She let it cry.                           _____

4. A hard, glinty coal.                      _____

5. Then the other.                           _____

6. As light as a feather.                    _____

7. The Overseer rode after her, hollerin'.   _____

8. And he flew away.                         _____

9. Nor could the Overseer.                   _____

10. They didn't sing.                        _____

*from "The People Could Fly," page E201*
*Virginia Hamilton*

## EXERCISE 2

### Understanding Sentence Fragments

Tell what is missing in each of the following sentence fragments—subject, verb, or subject and verb.

1. Stalled the car engine.

   _____

2. In the middle of the highway.

   _____

3. The dark clouds.

   _____

4. A long, narrow road.

   _____

5. Beyond the mountain ridge.

   _____

6. Lived in a small trailer by the highway.

   _____

7. Watched the rigs roll by on the road.

   _____

8. On the dusty road near town.

   _____

9. Bought the general merchandise store.

   _____

10. Tourists, townspeople, and truckers.

   _____

# EXERCISE 3

## Correcting Sentence Fragments

Correct each of the following sentence fragments. Make each fragment into a complete sentence by supplying the missing element(s).

1. At the roadside diner.

   _____

2. Ate scrambled eggs and toast.

   _____

3. Paid for breakfast.

   _____

4. The sign above the diner.

   _____

5. Down the road.

   _____

6. A bright sun.

   _____

7. The hills in the distance.

   _____

8. On the old radio.

   _____

9. Sang the verses out loud.

   _____

10. In his truck.

    _____

*Writing & Grammar*

Name: _____ Date: _____

**LESSON 63**

# Run-On Sentences

A **run-on sentence** is made up of two or more sentences that have been run together as if they were one complete thought. A run-on sentence can confuse the reader about where a thought starts or ends.

Take a look at the following examples of run-on sentences. In the first run-on, no punctuation mark is used between two complete sentences. In the second run-on, a comma is used incorrectly.

EXAMPLES
The drummer boy waited solemnly his heart pounded in his chest.

During the Civil War tens of thousands of young teenage boys joined the Confederate and Union armies, many of the boys served as drummers and buglers.

You can correct a run-on by dividing it into two separate sentences. Mark the end of each idea with a period, question mark, or exclamation point. Capitalize the first word of each new sentence.

EXAMPLE
The drummer boy waited solemnly. His heart pounded in his chest.

You can also correct a run-on by using a semicolon. The part of the sentence after the semicolon is not capitalized unless it is a proper noun or proper adjective. Use a semicolon to join two independent clauses only if they are very closely related.

EXAMPLE
During the Civil War tens of thousands of young teenage boys joined the Confederate and Union armies; many of the boys served as drummers and buglers.

## EXERCISE 1

### Identifying Run-on Sentences

Identify which of the following sentences are run-ons. If the sentence is correct, write *sentence*.

1. Rip van Winkle is a well-known character in American pop culture he is recognized in many books, cartoons, and movies.

   _____

2. He lived in the Catskill Mountains just before the Revolutionary War.

   _____

3. The children of the village love him they learned how to fly a kite and shoot marbles.

   _____

4. Rip did not like to work hard it was impossible to do his own work.

   _____

5. He fell asleep while on a walk in the woods.

   _____

6. Rip encountered a man dressed in antique Dutch fashion and drank some of his liquor.

   _____

7. He had slept for a very long time he slept for twenty years.

   _____

8. Rip returns to the village to find his wife has died only a few older citizens recognize him.

   _____

9. His daughter takes him into her house he resumes his previous lifestyle.

   _____

10. Rip has probably has a meeting with the ghost of Hendrick Hudson's crew.

    _____

# EXERCISE 2

## Correcting Run-on Sentences

Correct each of the following run-on sentences. Decide whether the run-on sentence can be corrected by dividing it into two separate sentences or by using a semicolon and forming one sentence.

1. A young woman rode with her husband and brother they were going to battle.

   _____

2. Buffalo Calf Road Woman rode next to her husband she did so with pride.

   _____

3. The Cheyenne were weary of the white man he didn't keep his promises.

   _____

4. The women of the Cheyenne were brave those in the Society of Quilters were
   the bravest of all.

   _____

5. A grizzly bear came into the camp he had a wounded leg.

   _____

6. The members of the Society of Quilters faced the bear they were unafraid.

   _____

7. The Cheyenne had teamed up with the Lakota people they were led by
   Crazy Horse.

   _____

8. Her brother is surrounded by the Crow scouts he was fighting for his life.

   _____

9. Buffalo Calf Road Woman rode into the fight she saved her brother.

   _____

10. The white men and Indians watched her act of bravery they cheered.

    _____

**LESSON 64**

# Wordy Sentences

A **wordy sentence** includes extra words and phrases that can be difficult, confusing, or repetitive to read. When you write, use only words necessary to make your meaning clear. Revise and edit your sentences so that they are not wordy or complicated. Review the following examples to learn about three different ways that you can correct wordy sentences.

Replace a group of words with one word.

EXAMPLES

| | |
|---|---|
| **wordy** | They cleaned the house **because of the fact that** guests were coming for Thanksgiving. |
| **revised** | They cleaned the house **because** guests were coming for Thanksgiving. |

Delete a group of unnecessary or repetitive words.

EXAMPLES

| | |
|---|---|
| **wordy** | **What I want to say is that** I enjoyed reading about the eccentric mother. |
| **revised** | I enjoyed reading about the eccentric mother. |
| **wordy** | The mother is a packrat, **and she doesn't throw anything away**. |
| **revised** | The mother is a packrat. |

Do not confuse a wordy sentence with a lengthy sentence. Writers vary their sentence lengths to create rhythm and add variety and liveliness to their work. Note the lengthy sentence underlined in the following excerpt. Even though the sentence is long, it does not contain extra words. The precise word choices in the long sentence make its meaning clear and create a vivid picture.

At the foot of these fairy mountains, the voyager may have descried the light smoke curling up from a village, whose shingle roofs gleam among the trees, just where the blue tints of the upland melt away into the fresh green of the nearer landscape. It is a little village, of great antiquity, having been founded by some of the Dutch colonists, in the early times of the province, just about the beginning of the government of the good Peter Stuyvesant, (may he rest in peace!) and there were some of the houses of the original settlers standing within a few years, built of small yellow bricks brought from Holland, having latticed windows and gable fronts, surmounted with weather-cocks.

*from "Rip Van Winkle," page E238*
*Washington Irving*

# EXERCISE 1

## Identifying Wordy Sentences

Read the following sentences. Underline any unnecessary words and phrases and any wordy constructions in each of the sentences.

1. The daughters were concerned due to the fact that the house was too messy.

2. The little boy did not want to clean his room and said that he wasn't going to do it.

3. On the dresser was a box full of jewelry, and there was a lot of jewelry in the box.

4. Jacyln arrived at dawn early in the morning.

5. She brought all sorts of different snacks, chips, pretzels, and crackers.

6. The old rusty typewriter was covered with dust and many parts had rusted.

7. Mr. Oliver carries a suitcase made out of leather.

8. The students were required to write a long and lengthy essay about the Civil War.

9. At 6 p.m. in the evening my friend is coming over to study.

10. I went to bed early in order to get lots of sleep.

# EXERCISE 2

## Correcting Wordy Sentences

The following paragraph contains some wordy sentences. Revise the paragraph by reducing the wordiness and making the meaning clear.

> Just because of the fact that Colin saves many different kinds of objects doesn't mean that he is peculiar. Many people are devoted collectors who collect all sorts of different things. These people usually became collectors in the first place because of the reason that they have a keen interest in something. Colin is interested in many things, including for example rare coins and stamps.

_____

_____

_____

_____

_____

_____

# EXERCISE 3

## Using Only Necessary Words

Write a paragraph about one of your more humorous habits, trying to use only necessary words. After writing, read your paragraph aloud to yourself, or ask a classmate to read it aloud while you listen. Correct any sentences that sound wordy.

_____

_____

_____

_____

_____

_____

_____

_____

_____

_____

_____